Science 6

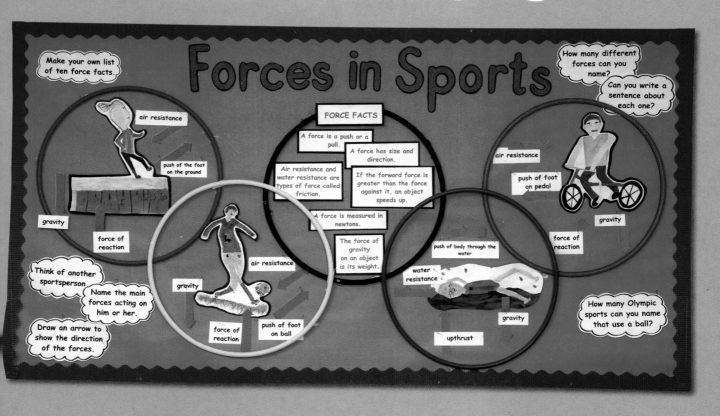

Carolyn Dale

Acknowledgements

A big thank you to everyone in the following Maidenhead primary schools who worked so hard to meet deadlines and to produce work of such a high quality for this book: Lowbrook, Knowl Hill, St Edmund Campion RC, Claires Court Schools, The Ridgeway, Waltham St Lawrence, White Waltham C of E and Woodlands Park, and to Juniper Hill Primary School, Flackwell Heath, Marlow. Without them there would be no book at all!

A very special thank you to Mary Gallop and Jean Davies of Lowbrook School who enthusiastically produced so much work for the book and lent their children to try out some of the activities; to Marion Bintcliffe and Judy Nott of The Ridgeway and Sonya Ludford of Knowl Hill for their enthusiasm and willingness to take on extra work at the last minute so that we could complete displays on time; to Shirley Craddock, a talented and creative ex-colleague who worked tirelessly in putting finishing touches to displays; to Zoë Parish, Paul Naish and Steve Forest for their patience and advice.

And last, but by no means least, I would like to thank my family and friends who have had to live with these books for a long time. I do hope that everyone – friends, family and colleagues – appreciate the final result!

from Reversible and Irreversible Change on page 32

Commissioning Editor: Zoë Parish   Editor: Elizabeth Miles   Cover Design: Sophie Pelham
Page Layout: Barbara Linton   Photography: Steve Forest   Illustrations: Ruth Murray

First published in 2008 by Belair Publications.

Every effort has been made to trace the copyright holders of material used in this publication. If any copyright holder has been overlooked, we should be pleased to make the necessary arrangements.

British Library Cataloguing in Publication Data. A catalogue record for this publication is available from the British Library.

ISBN 978-1-84191-466-4

Contents

Interdependence and Adaptation

These grids demonstrate the learning objectives covered in the activities within the theme. The curriculum references indicate the relevant programme of study (PoS) for a subject area unless otherwise stated.

	Learning Objectives	Curriculum References
Science (Page 6)		
Scientific Enquiry	Plan and carry out an enquiry into plant germination.	Sc1/2a-m
	Use computer simulations to monitor plant growth in different conditions.	Sc1/1a,b;2a-m; ICT PoS 1a;2a,c;4a; QCA ICT Unit 5F
Life Processes and Living Things (QCA Science Unit 6A)	Compare life processes of animals and plants.	Sc2/1a-c
	Know how living things adapt to their environment.	Sc2/5b,c
	Make and interpret food chains and webs.	Sc2/5d,e
	Make and interpret keys to sort living things.	Sc2/4a-c
Literacy (Page 8)		
Speaking	Debate what they would do if they suddenly became rich.	En1/1a-f;2a-e;3a-e
	Debate the pros and cons of people exploring the rainforest.	En1/1a-f;2a-e;3a-e
Understanding and Interpreting Texts	How people in real life or fiction have to adapt to situations.	En2/1a-d;2a-d;3a-g
Engaging with and Responding to Texts	Read/evaluate estate agents' advertisements.	En2/3a-g
Creating and Shaping Texts	Devise advertisements for animal homes/own homes/ school.	En3/1a-e;6a,b;9b-d
	Write diaries about a special change.	En3/1a-e;6a,b;9b,d
	Write a newspaper report of discovery of a new plant/animal.	En3/1a-e;2a-f;6a;7d
	Devise silly alliterative sentences for animals.	En3/1a-e;2a-f
	Devise a nonsense alphabet about animals using different parts of speech.	En3/1a-e;7a
	Write about the rainforest or other environment using different genres.	En3/1a-e;2a-f;6a,b;7a-d;8
Mathematics (Page 10)		
Understanding Shape	Translate, rotate and reflect shapes in four quadrants.	Ma3/3a-c; Ma2/4e; ICT PoS 1a,b;2b;5a-c
Using and Applying Mathematics	Present information from a database.	Ma3/1e-g; ICT PoS 1a-c; 2a;5a-c; QCA ICT Unit 5B
	Collect data about a pond or other natural habitat.	Ma3/1a-h;4a,b,e; ICT PoS 1a-c;2a;3b;4a-c;5a-c; QCA ICT Unit 5C
Handling Data	Convert data to appropriate graphs about plant growth.	Ma4/2a-f
Calculating	Devise equations for multi-step calculations about plant growth.	Ma2/4a,b
	Answer and ask questions involving calculations.	Ma2/1b,d,e,g,h,i; 3a,i,j;4a-c

Learning Objectives	Curriculum References
Design & Technology (Page 12)	
Design and make temporary shelters.	PoS 1a-d;2a-e;3a-c;4a,b; 5a-c; QCA DT Unit 6A
Art (Page 12)	
Design camouflage for different backgrounds.	PoS 1a-c;2a-c;3a,b; 4a,b;5a
Design and make a liana to represent living things in the forest.	PoS 1a-c;2a-c;4a-c;5a-d
History (Page 12)	
Study change in people's lives in Victorian times and how they adapted.	PoS 1a,b;2a-d;3;4a,b;5a-c
Look at change in buildings locally.	PoS 1a,b;4b;5c
MFL (Page 12)	
Name and identify countries on a map; choose one to talk about.	PoS 1a-g;2a-c;3a-g
Ask and answer questions about animals.	PoS 1a-g;2a;3a-g; QCA MFL Unit 6
Geography (Page 13)	
Identify rainforests/mountain environments on a world map.	PoS 1b;2a,c,d; QCA Geography Unit 15
Compare conditions in different environments, how and why they are changing.	PoS 3a-g;4a,b;5a,b; QCA Geography Unit 15
Discuss problems associated with change in an environment.	PoS 4a,b;5a,b
Find out how people and other living things adapt to a changing environment.	PoS 4a,b;5a,b
PSHCE (Page 13)	
Find/discuss facts about a selected changing environment.	PoS 2a,f,h,i,j,k;4b,f
Discuss how we can help to save wildlife.	PoS 2a,b,d,e,f,h
Find out about any local environmental projects.	PoS 2a,h
Discuss concerns when moving on to a new school.	PoS 1a,b,c,e;2c,f;4a,c,d,e,g; QCA Citizenship Unit 12
Discuss issues of responsibility to the world environment.	PoS 2a,d,h,k;4b,f;5d,h
Recognise results of a breakdown in a food chain.	PoS 2a
Music (page 13)	
Listen to music of the rainforests.	PoS 4a-d
Learn and perform songs of the rainforest or other environment.	PoS 1a-c;2a,b;3a-c;5a-e; QCA Music Unit 15

Interdependence and Adaptation

Starting Points

- Show pictures or watch a film of a range of familiar plants and animals. Ask the children to name the life processes of all living things. List the processes, then together select one plant and one animal. For each, name its habitat, how it carries out its life processes and decided how it is suited to its habitat.

Enquiry

- Find animals and plants in a local habitat. Draw them accurately on card, and then laminate. Find out how each animal or plant carries out its life processes, as above. For as many processes as possible, add information on how the animal or plant has adapted to its habitat.

- Use the laminated drawings to introduce energy flow in a food chain. Teach the convention as below, with arrows going from the producer (the green plant) to the consumer, e.g.

    leaves → earthworm → hedgehog

    plant (producer) → herbivore (prey) → carnivore (predator)

- Introduce vocabulary for the above chain or web. More able children could look for several links and convert them into a food web. Use the activity sheet on page 7.

Extension Activities

- Make up keys to sort out a collection of animals or plants from a range of habitats. Provide a key with some questions missing for children to complete. Ask them to draw keys in different ways.

- Remove one of the living things from a food chain. Ask the children to predict what would happen to all the others in the chain, both in the short term and long term.

- Study a single animal or plant and list the ways it is adapted to its environment and way of life, such as in the bat display shown.

- Play simulation plant growth and food chain games, such as 'Plant Force' and 'Sunny Meadows' at http://puzzling. caret.cam.ac.uk/.

Oak Tree City

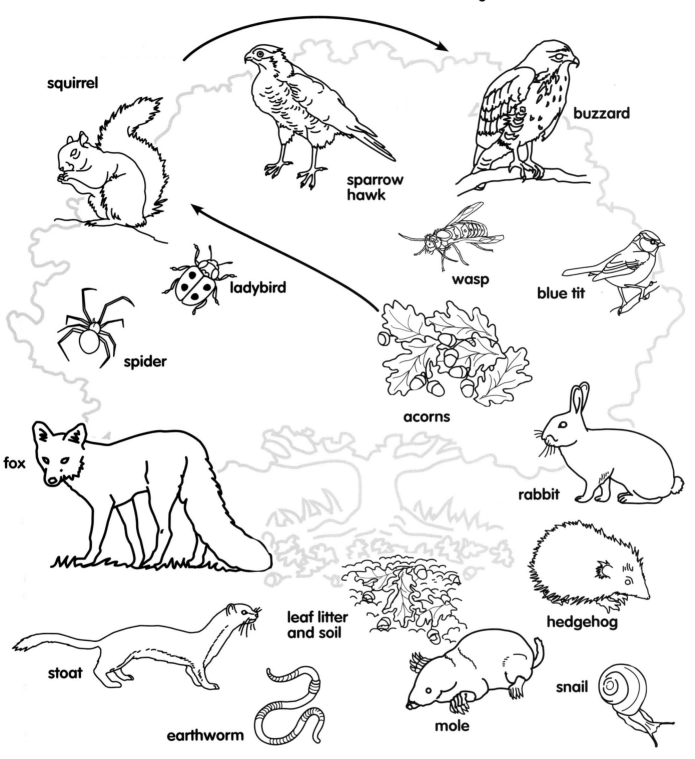

squirrel

sparrow hawk

buzzard

ladybird

wasp

blue tit

spider

acorns

fox

rabbit

hedgehog

leaf litter and soil

stoat

earthworm

mole

snail

This is Oak Tree City. Many different animals live on and under it.

A food chain shows what animals eat. In Oak Tree City each food chain begins with a plant – its leaves or acorns.

One food chain has been completed: acorns ⟶ squirrel ⟶ buzzard

Draw arrows to show other food chains in Oak Tree City. First, you need to find out what each animal eats.

Use a different colour to show each food chain.

Literacy

Reading and Writing

- Read and discuss how estate agents advertise houses for sale/to let. What sort of things do they highlight in their advertisements? Produce an advertisement to sell or let homes in a specific habitat, such as a rockpool (above).

- Write a diary about a change in life, such as moving house, school or a special holiday.

- Read stories in which people have to adapt to a new way of life or situation. Classics include *Alice's adventures in Wonderland*, *Peter Pan* and *Cinderella*. For modern literature, *The breadwinner* by Deborah Ellis (Oxford University Press) is a topical story in which 11-year-old Parvana's father is arrested by the Taliban. Other good stories include Lemony Snicket's novels (Egmont Books), *Driftwood* by Cathy Cassidy (Puffin Books), *Barnaby Grimes: curse of the nightwolf* by Paul Stewart and Chris Riddell (Corgi Children's) and *Alone on a wide wide sea* by Michael Morpurgo (HarperCollins Children's Books).

- Devise a class alphabet of wacky animals: 'In the rainforest there is … an ambitious ant acting angrily … a kicking koala kisses kindly' and so on. Include an adjective, noun, verb and adverb in each sentence.

Speaking and Listening

- A typical 4 square mile patch of rainforest contains as many as 1,500 species of flowering plants, 750 species of trees, 125 mammal species, 400 species of birds, 100 species of reptiles, 60 species of amphibians, and 150 different species of butterflies. There are many species still to be discovered. Ask the children to imagine they go to a rainforest and discover an amazing new plant or animal. Use the activity sheet on page 9 as a starting point to plan a radio interview. Encourage children to use a literary genre to write about it, e.g. poem, narrative, recount or newspaper report that includes a scientist's view of how it lives and survives.

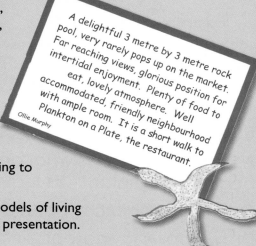

- Set groups the task of inventing an animal and producing and presenting to the rest of the class different types of writing about it.

- Link with DT, Art and ICT by setting up a rainforest scene, making models of living things in their homes, and discussing how to produce a PowerPoint® presentation.

- Debate the pros and cons of exploring the rainforest.

Interdependence and Adaptation

PAROGUIN GIGANTIOSAUR

The imaginary *Paroguin Gigantiosaur* has just been discovered. It was thought to be extinct. Is it an animal? Is it a plant? What does it look like? Where does it live?

Draw a picture of it in its natural habitat here. Remember to label your picture.

Work with a friend. Plan a radio interview in which you discuss your discovery. Make the interview last for no more than 4 minutes. It should be really interesting and make people want to know more about it.

NOW!

Find out about a real animal that is endangered. Present your findings to the class.

Maths

Using and Applying

- Investigate a hedgerow. Identify the species of plants and animals; measure the area; record the light and temperature, height of plants; note where the species are found.

- Assist children in collecting data about a habitat, such as a pond (surface area, depth at different places, distance across, shape and perimeter). Draw a plan of it to scale and, if possible, use sensors to monitor temperature changes.

Handling Data

- Encourage children to collect data about plants

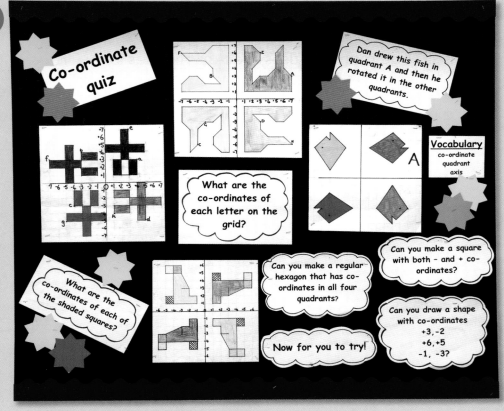

in a field. Put hoops down in different places (e.g. light and shady areas; areas used a lot and those seldom used; wet and drier areas; where there is a lot of soil and where there is less). Ask the children to identify the different plants and their frequency in each hoop. Look for patterns and complete sentences about their observations, such as 'Dandelions grow most where… .' Collate all the information and store it on a database.

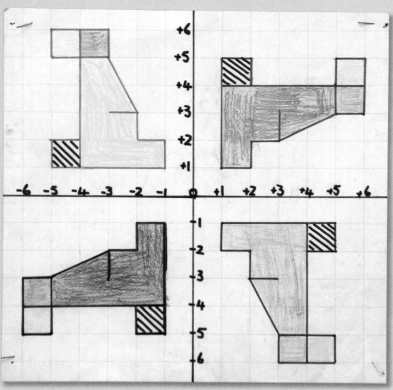

Calculating

- Imagine a strange plant and draw or make a collage of it. Explain how it carries out its life processes – encourage the children to be imaginative. Draw it twice as big and twice as small and make up equations about its reproduction. For example, if it has two life cycles a year and each time produces an average of 60 seeds, 25% of which survive, how long before there are 1000 of the species? Repeat, using the activity sheet on page 11.

Understanding Shape

- Ask the children to draw a shape in one quadrant of a grid and write down the co-ordinates for each vertex. Translate and reflect the shape in other quadrants and ask the children to write the vertex co-ordinates for each shape drawn. Do the same for flower and leaf shapes and simple animal outlines. Link with ICT by using a graphics program to draw shapes, e.g. petals, and develop them into flowers, using repeat instructions. See the display above for ideas.

Work it out!

This strange mammal uses special tentacles to feel its way along the forest floor.

Calculate the following:

It has 9 tentacles. How many tentacles in a family of 198?

They breed 3 times a day. The average number of offspring each time is 23. How many will there be after 7 days?

Each offspring eats 25 square cm of leaves each hour. How many square cm does it eat in a day?

A family of creatures needs to take in 350 ml of water each day. How much water is this in the month of April?

A survey counted 368560 of these creatures on 1 June. A drought caused their food of leaves to die and so there were 40% fewer by the end of June. How many survived?

It has a heart that beats 96 times each minute. How many beats is this per day?

NOW!

Devise some more mathematical questions about the creature.

Design & Technology

- Introduce the scenario of an explorer in a given location. Provide details of the environment, including its location and the materials available. Design a temporary shelter, either a model or life-sized to fit two people. If possible, make a bivouac using natural materials. Test it to find out if it will stand up to the rain and wind.

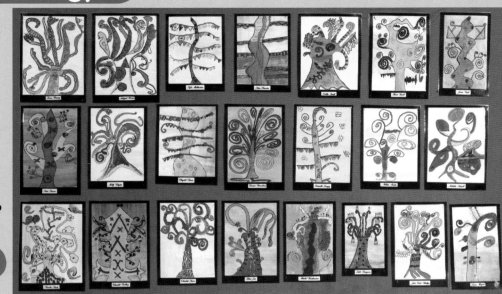

Art

- A liana is a vine. Design one for decoration, and include representations of living things in the rainforest, such as different leaves, lizards and butterflies.

- Study how animals are camouflaged in their natural environment. Paint two identical animals. Paint two backgrounds – one in which it is camouflaged and one in which it is easy to find.

- Paint a picture of a habitat, then cut it into sections, e.g. squares, and mix them up before putting them together again to make a new picture. In the display on the left, *Tiger in a tropical storm* by Henri Rousseau (1844–1910) was copied and rearranged as shown.

- Look at Klimt's painting, *The tree of life*. Create an imaginary plant and paint it in the style of Klimt (1862–1918), as shown in the display above.

History

- Find out about influential people from Victorian times who caused change. Ask them to look for people to put under the headings of: inventors; people who helped others; people who caused changes in social life; writers; composers and painters. Put them on a timeline of the Victorian period.

- Compare the life of a child in 1837 and in 1901. Ask them to list how things changed using the following headings: homes, schools, hobbies, streets, clothes, travel. How did people adapt to these changes in lifestyle?

- Look locally for Victorian influences in buildings. Compare their size, structure and the materials used. How has a local Victorian house changed today from when it was first built?

MFL

- Name and identify on a map the countries relevant to the languages they are studying. Identify their position in relation to the UK using directional language. Ask children to devise questions about the position of a country. Extend to include questions about the country's people, animals and conditions, e.g. environments.

Geography

- Identify different mountain environments on a map. Collect data about each. Find out how each is changing and why.

- Find out about the lives of the indigenous people of the rainforest (such as the Yanomami people of Brazil) or a mountain environment – link with music (for ideas see the Music section below). Discover how they are adapting to change, and what resources they rely on.

- Find some facts about the rainforest to promote discussion, such as the rate at which trees are being removed and the effects on the numbers and types of animals that live there. Make a display and include facts from secondary sources, as shown above.

PSHCE

- Find facts about the destruction of the rainforests and how it affects food chains and the people, animals and plants living in the rainforests. There are many informative websites. The following are suitable for children to research: www.nationalforest.org; www.woodland-trust.org.uk; www.treeforall.org.uk/ (activities and games). For more rainforest facts try: www.rain-tree.com or www.nature.org/rainforests/.

- Discuss things we can do to help animals or wildlife (e.g. plant a tree, build a pond for frogs, start composting, ban harmful chemicals in the garden, grow own vegetables and fruit). Then do it!

- Hold a circle time about the changes involved in moving on to the next school. What will be the same and different? What difficulties do they foresee? Who can help them?

Music

- Listen to 'music' of the rainforest. See www.cyberbee.com/rain.html which leads into other useful sites appropriate for children. Try to identify the living and non-living things making the sounds. Encourage the children to think of ways to represent them, and to put them together to make their own 'rainforest music'. Add descriptive words and phrases to the performance. Allow time for practice, then perform to other classes.

Micro-organisms

These grids demonstrate the learning objectives covered in the activities within the theme. The curriculum references indicate the relevant programme of study (PoS) for a subject area unless otherwise stated.

	Learning Objectives	Curriculum References
Science (Page 16)		
Enquiry	Plan and investigate rates of food decay.	Sc1/2b-m
	Select instruments for measuring temperature.	Sc1/2e,f,g
Life Processes and Living Things (QCA Science Unit 6B)	Know how micro-organisms affect health.	Sc2/5f
	Know how micro-organisms are used in food manufacture.	Sc2/5f
	Know the different ways in which food is preserved to slow the growth of micro-organisms.	Sc2/5f
Literacy (Page 18)		
Speaking/Listening and Responding	Use and recall specialist vocabulary in discussion about illnesses/micro-organisms.	En1/1a,c,e;2a-e
Drama	Make up a play about an attack of micro-organisms.	En1/4a-d;11a-c
Creating and Shaping Texts	Create an imaginary microbe/micro-organism.	En3/1a-e;2a-f
	Write instructions using the imperative.	En3/1b-e;6a
	Find information about famous scientists.	En2/3a-e;9b;En1/1a-f
	Find and display facts about micro-organisms.	En2/1a-e;3a-e;9b
Presentation	Present information about micro-organisms in different ways, such as leaflets, letters, information sheets, newspaper report.	En3/1a-e;2a-f;6a,b;8; ICT PoS 2a,b;3a,b;4a,c
Mathematics (Page 20)		
Counting and Understanding Numbers	Calculate differences between positive and negative numbers.	Ma2/2a
Measuring	Sequence temperatures including below zero.	Ma3/4b;Ma2/2a
	Measure temperatures, including using sensors and make generalisations of change over time.	Ma3/4a,b; ICT PoS 1a-c;4a-c;5a-c; QCA ICT Unit 5F
	Measure change in volume and mass over time.	Ma3/1a;4a
Handling Data	Interpret information from a line graph and suggest reasons for change.	Ma4/2f
	Draw and interpret line graphs.	Ma4/1a-e;2b,c,e,f

Micro-organisms

Learning Objectives	Curriculum References
PSHCE (Page 22)	
Know about personal hygiene and take responsibility for it.	PoS 3b
Explain how to care for teeth.	PoS 3b
Know about the causes of plaque.	PoS 3b
Design & Technology (Page 22)	
Recognise safe procedures for food safety and hygiene.	PoS 2f
Make bread/biscuits.	PoS 2a,b,c,f; QCA Design & Technology Unit 5B
Art (Page 22)	
Use an ICT package to create shapes and patterns of micro-organisms.	PoS 1a-c;2a,c;3a,b;5c; QCA ICT Unit 5A
Present a display of a fridge at a dangerous temperature.	PoS 1a-c;2a-c
Use actual micro-organisms to stimulate pattern and design in art.	PoS 1a-c;2a-c;3a,b; 4a-c;5a-c
PE (Page 22)	
Know how to maintain a clean and healthy body.	PoS 4d
Design a sequence for movement – to represent attack of microbes.	PoS 8a,b
History (Page 24)	
Record diseases caused by micro-organisms in the past (Black Death, plague, typhus, etc) and how they were treated.	PoS 1a;2a-d;3;4a,b
Find out about scientists who pioneered treatment of diseases caused by microbes.	PoS 1a,b;2a-d;4a; QCA History Unit 12
Know how research into microbes has affected our lives since 1948.	PoS 1a;2a,b;4a,b; QCA History Unit 13
Geography (Page 24)	
Know the range of diseases in different parts of the world and conditions that cause them, such as lifestyle, weather, facilities, etc.	PoS 2c,d,f;3a-f;5a; QCA Geography Unit 16
Monitor environmental conditions.	PoS 1a,c,e;2a,d,f; QCA ICT Unit 5F
Music (Page 24)	
Sing songs about diseases in past.	PoS 1a;3a,b;4d; QCA Units 17 and 21
Compose lyrics, using familiar tunes.	PoS 1a;2a,b; QCA Unit 19

Micro-organisms

Our Daily Bread

Wheat needs heat, light and water to germinate and grow

irreversible change

FLOUR

Wheat is ground into flour

flour + sugar + water + heat + yeast = dough (a micro-organism)

leave dough

yeast cells divide and release carbon dioxide gas

yeast cells

cook

eat it

an irreversible change

Holes made by carbon dioxide

The dough rises

Science

Starting Points

● Find out what the children know about micro-organisms through discussion, a 'True or false?' quiz or draw a micro-organism and ask groups to write all that they know around it. Focus their attention on good and bad micro-organisms by showing cheese and yoghurt or another food that is made using micro-organisms and by sneezing into a handkerchief. Explain that an alternative term for micro-organism is 'microbe', and introduce the words 'bacterium'/'bacteria' and 'virus' as these are scientific and common terms. 'Germ' is a colloquial term and so should not be used as an alternative. Explain that 'micro-' means very small. Discuss size.

Enquiry

● Select a variety of foods such as cheese, different fruit, butter, meat and bread. Ask the children to predict what will happen to them over time. Put the foods in separate sealed transparent containers, such as jars or bags, which are subsequently **never** opened. Keep a diary of the changes.

 After the investigation, the containers should be thrown away safely, unopened.

● Compare the containers of foods. Discuss the speed of decay and reasons why some foods apparently decay. Where have the micro-organisms come from? Refer back to the eighteenth century when scientists thought that decay came from the food itself and had no idea that micro-organisms existed in the air because they could not see them. Look at the decay on the foods through the bag using a hand lens to give an idea of how small they are. Even through the lens they are still very tiny.

Extension Activities

● Find out about useful micro-organisms and how they are used in the making of yoghurt, cheese or bread. Make a flow chart showing the stages in its manufacture. Together, list and collate suitable scientific words and phrases for the display. Encourage children to include as many as possible in the display, as on the Daily Bread cycle shown above.

● Use secondary sources to find diseases caused by microbes. Provide copies of the activity sheet on page 17, on which they can note the diseases. The activity also encourages them to think of ways in which the spread of disease-causing microbes can be stopped.

Evil Mr Mike Robe!

Mr Mike Robe is at it again! He knows how to spread diseases in all sorts of ways ...

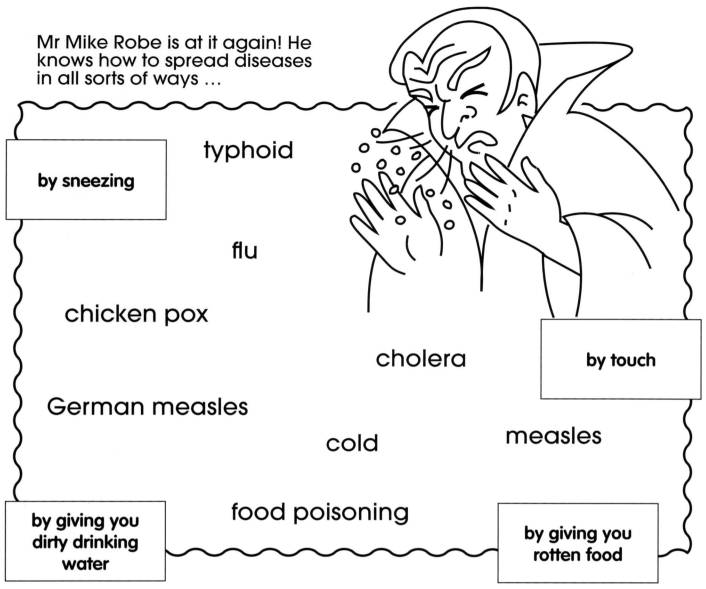

by sneezing

typhoid

flu

chicken pox

cholera

by touch

German measles

cold

measles

by giving you dirty drinking water

food poisoning

by giving you rotten food

Draw a line from each disease to the ways in which he can spread it.

NOW!

Choose one question and present the information you find to your group or class.

- How can we stop microbes getting to our teeth?

- Are all micro-organisms harmful?

- What are bacteria?

- What are viruses?

- How is malaria spread?

Watch out 'bugs' about!

Literacy

Speaking and Listening

- Encourage the children, in pairs, to mime and list illnesses and other problems they have had with their bodies, such as broken legs or arms, colds, headaches, coughs and tummy upsets. Through discussion sort them into problems 'caused by germ spreading' and 'not caused by germ'. Ensure children understand that 'germ' is a general term, not a scientific one.

- Split the class into two groups: the mean microbes team and the useful microbe team. Ask each team to find information about their different types of micro-organisms. It will help to remind them of the essential vocabulary, such as bacteria, virus, microbe and micro-organism. Discuss headings they could use to organise their information, e.g. types, size, life cycle, effects, uses. Each team writes text about what they have found out. The teams then take turns to present and answer questions about their text, while those listening can make notes of the essential points.

- Present a play entitled 'Tooth Attack' in which evil microbes attack two different mouths, one where the teeth have been brushed and the other where they have not. Include a sound accompaniment.

Reading and Writing

- On a large outline of a human body, position labels to show the effects of micro-organisms on different parts of the body, e.g. label the stomach with 'stomach upsets'; label spots with 'measles' or 'chicken pox', and label a red nose 'cold'. Add information about each disease.

- Provide children with the activity sheet on page 19. After they have completed the activity, they can use it as inspiration to invent their own imaginary micro-organism. Ask them to draw it and write information about its lifestyle and where it exists. Present the children's work as a display, as shown above.

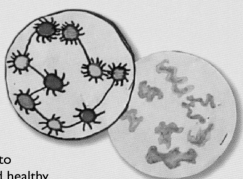

- In groups, make up a microbe quiz or board game 'Get rid of the microbes' or a game in which good microbes take you up or forward and bad ones send you down or back.

- Write instructions, using the imperative, for one of the following: how to store foods safely to prevent them from rotting; how to keep clean and healthy.

Micro-organisms

Sajid's Micro-spectacular

This is a Micro-spectacular, a type of micro-organism that Sajid imagined.

The Micro-spectacular is an amazing creature. I found it one day when I was digging in the compost heap. I spotted it when I turned over a pile of rotting leaves. It was about the size of a large ant or worm, so quite easy to see.

'Is it alive?' I wondered. As I watched, nothing happened – no movement at all, so I carried on digging. But then out of the corner of my eye I saw it doing a most amazing thing! It grew and grew! Then there was a plopping sound as it split into two. The two new ones looked like identical twins. It had reproduced itself! I watched, amazed, as it did the same thing again ... and again. Before I knew it, I was surrounded by millions of them – all wriggling about like an army. My heart began to race! They might get hungry and eat me alive! I ran to the house and watched from a safe distance. The compost heap began to steam. The Micro-spectaculars were reproducing at a fantastic rate. They were real, living things! 'They are aliens,' I thought. 'They are about to take over the world. Should I phone the police?'

Although Sajid's Micro-spectacular is imaginary, some of the facts he has given about micro-organisms are true. Other information he gave is not true of real micro-organisms. Underline in red two true facts he has written about micro-organisms.

Put a blue ring around two things that are untrue.

NOW!

Make up an imaginary micro-organism that lives in food. Is it hostile or friendly? Describe how it is dangerous or useful.

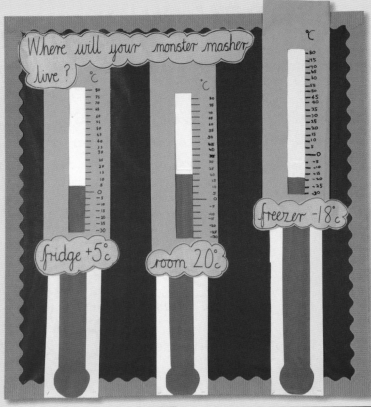

Maths

Measuring

- Let the children examine a thermometer and show how to use it by finding the temperatures of hot water, cold water and the interior of a fridge.

> ⚠️ CAREFUL SUPERVISION IS REQUIRED

- Make a number line for a thermometer with a scale that measures + and − temperatures, as shown in the display.

  You will need: 2 sheets of A4 scrap paper – one for the main part of the thermometer (A) and one for the scale (B), plus a small piece for cutting.

  1. Fold sheet A twice as shown to make the main part of the thermometer.

  2. Cut out a thin channel down the fold and open out.

  3. Now fold sheet B lengthways to make a thin narrow strip. Tape or glue the edges. This will be a section that slides. Colour the lower half of the strip red to indicate the alcohol in the thermometer.

  4. Put the B (the strip) behind sheet A and cut and stick some small strips of paper across B to hold B in place while allowing it to slide up and down.

  5. On the front write a scale from −25°C at the bottom to +25°C at the top as shown on the display.

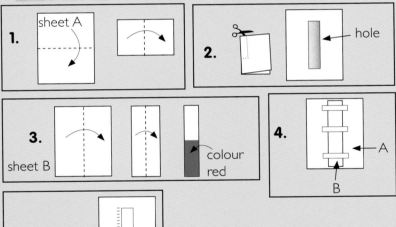

Now try it out. Slide B so that the red section is level with the temperature of the classroom. Then ask children to move it to show the temperature of freezing water.

- Extend work on negative numbers into work on co-ordinates in the four quadrants. Ask the children to mark points using positive and negative numbers and to connect them to form shapes.

Handling Data

- Carry out a survey of breads to find out which is the most popular. Display the results on a slice of bread shape. Measure mass and volume of different loaves. Predict how each of these will change (if at all) over a week. REMEMBER to keep breads in sealed containers in case of decay. Check the loaves regularly and record what happens on a table. Convert to a graph showing varying rates of decay. Ask the children to discuss the results, and whether brown or white breads appear to decay more quickly.

Understanding Number

- Give the children copies of the activity sheet on page 21. After completing the activities the children could complete their own monster masher drawing with problems to solve.

Micro-organisms

Monster problems

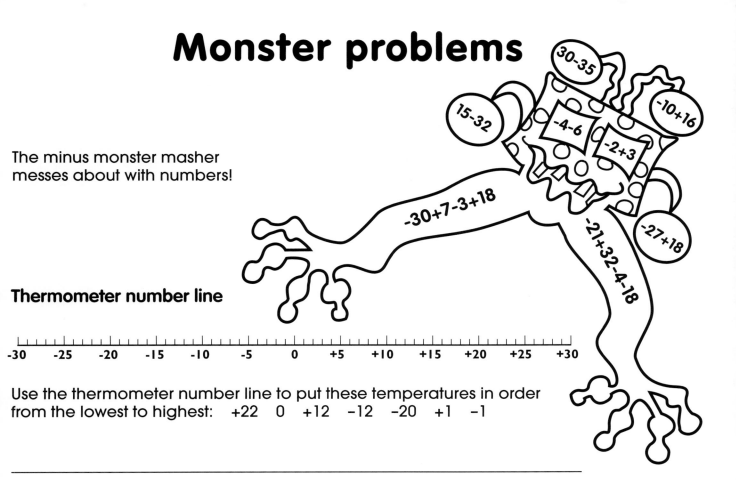

The minus monster masher messes about with numbers!

Thermometer number line

-30   -25   -20   -15   -10   -5   0   +5   +10   +15   +20   +25   +30

Use the thermometer number line to put these temperatures in order from the lowest to highest: +22   0   +12   −12   −20   +1   −1

_____

Up or down!

Calculate how many degrees there are between each pair of temperatures below.
Say whether the temperature is going up or down.

+7° and −1°C   The difference is _____ degrees. The temperature is going _____

−12° and +12°C   The difference is _____ degrees. The temperature is going _____

0° and −22°C   The difference is _____ degrees. The temperature is going _____

+14° and −3°C   The difference is _____ degrees. The temperature is going _____

Solve a monster problem!

The minus monster masher has blood that freezes at −8°C and boils at +10°C. His only food is winter worms that breed at 4°C. He wants to live in your house. Where should you put him so that he is safe and can get plenty of food?

CLUE: Make sure that his blood doesn't freeze or boil – or HE WILL DIE!

How many places can you think of?

PSHCE

- Examine a variety of foods that are preserved in different ways. Discuss why each method works. How many ways are peas or beans preserved? Are other foods preserved in various ways? Create a display, as shown above, with food types grouped according to the method used.

- Describe a place where micro-organisms could multiply rapidly, such places in a kitchen. Use the activity sheet on page 23 for ideas.

- Find out which foods cause tooth decay. Design posters and organise demonstrations to show how to prevent tooth decay, e.g. how to brush your teeth and how often. Find out about plaque and its causes.

Design & Technology

- Make bread or biscuits using a recipe and adding different ingredients to make it more interesting (see also Reversible and Irreversible Change, pages 26–35).

- Make yoghurt or cheese and talk about the microbes involved. Write the recipe for others to follow, perhaps with a new flavour.

Art

- As micro-organisms are so varied in structure, they offer a good starting point for artwork such as collages, paintings and repeated designs. Search for micro-organisms at www.fotosearch.com for lots of photos of real microbes. Look at these or other images, focusing on their design, shapes, patterns and colours. Encourage children to create their own abstract version of them.

- Work in groups to create a picture showing the temperature range in a cupboard at which micro-organisms grow and multiply at a fast rate (between 10 and 70°C). Each group member can create his or her own micro-organism for display, with a central image of a thermometer showing the danger temperature range. Give the display a title such as 'Danger Zone'.

PE

- Work in groups to devise ways of moving like a microbe in different situations, e.g. in different temperatures or amounts of moisture and when they are met by medicines!

- Ask the children to think of a visit to a swimming pool and discuss issues of hygiene, e.g. how verrucas and athlete's foot are spread and how they can be avoided.

Micro-organisms

Ronnie's rotten restaurant

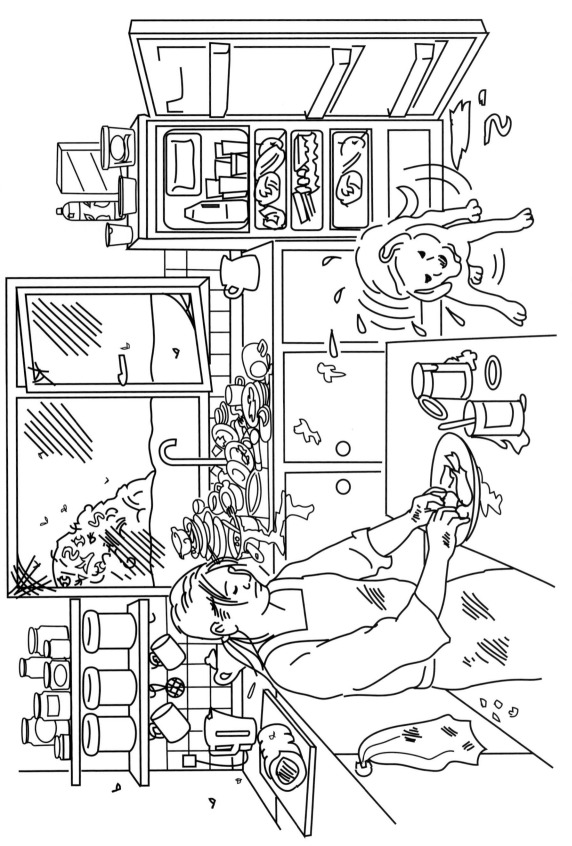

Where in this kitchen do you think micro-organisms are multiplying most quickly?

Make a list of things Ronnie should do to stop micro-organisms growing in this kitchen.

Imagine you're a health inspector – write a formal letter to Ronnie explaining how she should look after her kitchen.

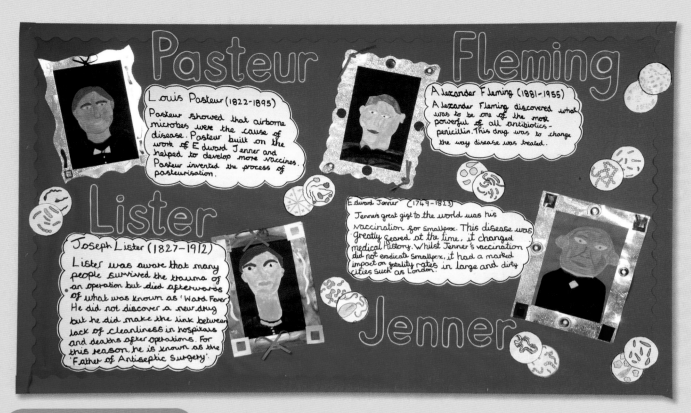

History

- Introduce the names of famous scientists who were instrumental in recognising the importance of micro-organisms in causing diseases, e.g. Louis Pasteur (1822–1895), Joseph Lister (1827–1912) (see activity sheet on page 25), Edward Jenner (1749–1823) and Alexander Fleming (1881–1955). In pairs, select one scientist to research using the Internet and books. Ask the children to record their findings as a PowerPoint® presentation, leaflet, zigzag books, poster or cartoon strip. Alternatively, display the children's text with illustrations as above.

- Ask children to imagine they are Louis Pasteur or another famous scientist and complete one of the following: write a letter telling another person of a famous discovery the artist made; hold a lecture to tell others of a discovery; write and design a leaflet about their work; or compose a newspaper report about a discovery.

- Find out about diseases caused by micro-organisms in the past (the Black Death, the plague, etc.) and how they were treated. What were people's beliefs about diseases at that time?

Geography

- Find out about diseases in different parts of the world and the difficulties in treating them, such as environment, poverty and access to medicine. Examples are typhoid, cholera, malaria and tuberculosis. Mark the countries where the diseases are common on a world map.

- Select a disease that is common in another country. Ask the children to find out as much about the disease and the country as possible and the conditions that make it spread. Ask them to suggest ways in which it could be controlled.

- Use sensors to monitor change in temperature over a period of time. Ask the children to take readings in places where micro-organisms are not wanted or are wanted, e.g. in the fridge, a compost heap. Investigate the use of thermostats to keep temperatures constant in fridges. (Link this with the Maths activities on page 20.)

Music

- Sing 'Ring a ring o' roses' and investigate its origins. Tap out its rhythm and devise their own song to sing to the same rhythm.

Micro-organisms

Joseph Lister and antiseptics

Look at the information about a famous scientist, Joseph Lister. He discovered ways to stop his patients getting infections from micro-organisms after operations.

Cut out each section and put them in order to tell a short story about his life and work.

He noticed that after operations more than half his patients died of **blood poisoning**, caused by their **wounds** becoming infected. How could he stop this infection?	Perhaps even more patients would survive if **surgeons** kept their hands clean, so he insisted that all surgeons washed their hands before operations. Again, the death rate fell.	He read about the work of Louis Pasteur. He thought one of Louis' ideas might be true – that infections were caused by harmful **microbes** in the air that got inside the body.	Could **carbolic acid** be killing the microbes in the sewage? Could it kill microbes in wounds too?
He presented his findings to the British Medical Council in 1869.	So he decided to try it out during an **operation** on an 11-year-old boy with a compound fracture of his leg.	Joseph Lister lived from 1827 to 1912. He was born in the county of Essex, the son of a corn merchant. The family were Quakers.	Lister put carbolic acid on swabs and on stitches to close up the boy's wound. The boy lived. It was a promising start and so he continued to use it.
Joseph Lister is remembered today as the pioneer of **antiseptics** in medicine and so the saver of many lives in his time and in ours.	Before taking up medicine, he studied fine arts at university. In 1856, he became an assistant surgeon in an Edinburgh hospital where he carried out many **amputations** of arms and legs.	He found out about a **chemical** called **carbolic acid** that had been used to treat **sewage** to produce clean water.	If microbes were the cause of **infections**, and if he could find a way to kill them, more patients might survive.

Make sure you understand the meanings of the words in bold. Make a glossary of these words.

Make up a drama to show what it was like in hospitals in Lister's day. How would you feel if you were a patient then?

Reversible and Irreversible Change

These grids demonstrate the learning objectives covered in the activities within the theme. The curriculum references indicate the relevant programme of study (PoS) for a subject area unless otherwise stated.

	Learning Objectives	Curriculum References
Science (Page 28)		
Enquiry	Suggest ideas about how to solve a problem about cleaning water.	Sc1/1a;2a,b
	Use science skills to clean dirty water.	Sc1/1a,b; 2a,b,c,e,f,h,i,j,k,l,m
Materials and their Properties (QCA Science Unit 6D)	Sort changes into reversible and irreversible.	Sc3/2d,f,g
	Describe characteristics of different changes.	Sc3/2a-d,f,g
	Explain how to reverse changes.	Sc3/2a,b
	Know how temperature affects different materials.	Sc3/2b,c
	Know how to separate materials.	Sc3/3a-e
	Know about changes in everyday life, including the water cycle.	Sc2/2e
Literacy (Page 30)		
Speaking	Debate causes of global warming.	En1/3a-e; QCA Citizenship Unit 11
	Interview a person involved with cooking food/a fireman.	En1/2b,e;9b; QCA Citizenship Unit 04
Drama	Act different scientific changes.	En1/4a-d
Understanding and Interpreting Texts	Find out about volcanoes.	En2/2b;5a-g
Engaging with and Responding to Texts	Read stories of witches and wizards by famous authors.	En2/2b;9b
Creating and Shaping Texts	Design a graffiti wall for scientific changes.	En3/1a-e
	Use language structures to describe flames/ice.	En3/1a-e;2a-f;9a
	Write a mystery/adventure story about the 'ice hand'.	En3/1a-e;2a-f;9a
	Devise a report about how to make biscuits/bread.	En3/1a-e;6a
	Correct a piece of writing about a science enquiry.	En3/3;4c-f
Mathematics (Page 32)		
Using and Applying Mathematics	Compare mass and volume before and after burning.	Ma3/1a-h;4a,b,d
Measuring	Measure volumes of solids and liquids.	Ma3/1a;4a,b
	Measure time and mass.	Ma3/1a;4a,b
	Convert measurements to larger and smaller units.	Ma3/1a;4a,b

Reversible and Irreversible Change

Learning Objectives	Curriculum References
Design & Technology (Page 34)	
Make a fizzy rocket or volcano.	PoS 1a-d;2a,b,d,e;4a
Make candles from pieces of crayon.	PoS 2a,f;4a
Evaluate types of biscuits and design own.	PoS 1d;2a,b,c,f;3a,b,c;5b; QCA DT Unit 5D
Design and make containers from clay.	PoS 1a-d;2a,d,e,f;3a,c;4a,b
Make coloured ice lollies.	PoS 1a-d;2a,d,e,f;3a,c;4a,b
Make plastic and use to design objects.	PoS 1a-d;2a,b,f;3a,c;
Design and make a firebird that moves a part of its body.	PoS 1a-d;2a-f;3a-c;4a-d
Art (Page 34)	
Use old plastic bags to design clothes and accessories	PoS 1a-c;2a-c;3a,b;4a-c;5a-c
Design a 2D or 3D firebird from textiles.	PoS 1a-c;2a-c;3a,b;4a; QCA Art Unit 5C
Design a firebird from fiery words for head, body, wings and tail.	PoS 1b;2c;3a,b;5a
Select a safe liquid and some materials to make a coloured witches' spell.	PoS 1a;2c;3a,b;4a,b;5a
PSHCE (Page 34)	
Know about a range of changes on the planet in own area.	PoS 1e
Discuss change in personal lives.	PoS 1a-c,e;2c,f;4a-d,g;5a-c; QCA Citizenship Unit 12
Investigate the dangers of burning manufactured fabrics.	PoS 3e
Suggest ways to reduce pollution.	PoS 1a; 2a
PE (Page 34)	
Use music and stimuli to devise a fire dance.	PoS 1a,b;6a,b; QCA PE Unit 22
Move like flames – show how they spark and spread.	PoS 1b;6b
Tell story in group movement of a fire and how it is extinguished.	PoS 1b;2a;6a,b; QCA PE Unit 22
Music (Page 34)	
Use symbols to represent different volumes and pitch.	PoS 2a,b;4c
In groups devise music for a witch's chant when making a spell.	PoS 1a;2a,b;3a-c; QCA Music Unit 21

Reversible and Irreversible Change

Science

Starting Points

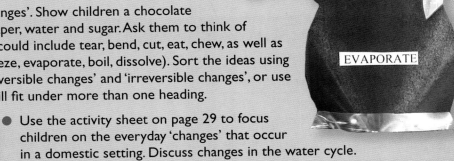

- Recap on previous work about 'changes'. Show children a chocolate biscuit, a metal object, a piece of paper, water and sugar. Ask them to think of ways to change each of them. This could include tear, bend, cut, eat, chew, as well as scientific processes (melt, burn, freeze, evaporate, boil, dissolve). Sort the ideas using these headings: 'changing shape', 'reversible changes' and 'irreversible changes', or use a Venn diagram as some changes will fit under more than one heading.

- Use the activity sheet on page 29 to focus children on the everyday 'changes' that occur in a domestic setting. Discuss changes in the water cycle.

Enquiry

- Show children saltwater with pebbles and sand in it. Discuss how they could clean it so that it is safe to drink.

- Provide equipment for them to try out their ideas. Include a range of sieves (can be homemade), some funnels (homemade from bottles), some filters (use kitchen towels or other absorbent paper), a variety of containers and perhaps some candles in a sand tray for heating.

- Ask groups to devise a plan to purify their water. They should write each stage on different pieces of paper, so they can reorder them if necessary. Encourage them to share their plans with other groups before carrying them out.

- Evaluate the methods and suggest improvements. Display their final method as shown.

> ⚠ **SAFETY WARNING:** Do not drink the water!

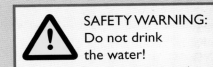

Extension Activities

- List the ingredients of a chocolate biscuit. How many ingredients can be recovered? (Only the chocolate.) Explain that cooking is irreversible, but chocolate can be melted and cooled so the change is reversible. Note that any change from a liquid to a solid is called freezing. So melted chocolate can be changed back to a solid by freezing it. Try different cooking activities and say if the changes are reversible or irreversible.

- Carry out other chemical changes, e.g. place a digestion tablet in water; mix a weak acid, such as vinegar or lemon juice with an alkali, such as baking powder or bicarbonate of soda; stir up fresh yeast with sugar and warm water. In each case, ask the children to note the gas produced. Explain that once gas is released we cannot recover the ingredients.

- Set challenges for the children to investigate: 'Does tomato ketchup freeze in the freezer?' (liquids containing oil will not freeze) 'Can you make coloured ice balloons/ice lollies?' 'How can you stop ice melting?' etc. This is a revision of activities from Book 5 (page 30).

The Birthday party

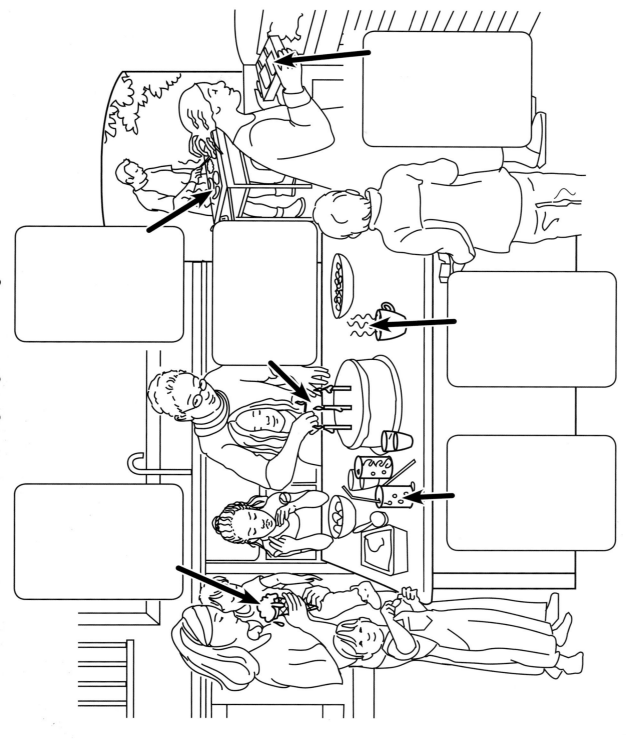

There are different changes happening to things in this picture of a party.

Here are some things for you to add to the picture:

1. In each box, write the name of the process. Choose from these:

   • evaporation
   • melting
   • condensation
   • freezing
   • burning

2. In each box, also describe how the thing is changing.

3. Colour each box lightly. If the change is reversible, colour it red. If the change is irreversible, colour it blue.

• Reversible and Irreversible Change • Belair Curricular-Links Science 6

Literacy

Reading and Writing

- Make a graffiti wall as shown. Put on the wall all the scientific changes children can think of. Encourage them to write the words in a descriptive way, e.g. 'boiling' to look hot. Choose one a week throughout the teaching of the theme. Ask the children to write a definition for that word and give as many examples as they can of the 'change'.

- Look carefully at a candle flame and describe it in detail: where and what colours are in the flame; its movement; any changes that occur. Display hot, fiery words and phrases as flames and smoke.

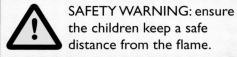 **SAFETY WARNING:** ensure the children keep a safe distance from the flame.

- Make a frozen hand by filling a plastic glove with water and freezing it for two days. Take off the glove to leave the ice hand. Use as a stimulus for a mystery story or newspaper report, e.g. 'Where has it come from?'

- Read books that include spells and 'changes' such as the Harry Potter series by J.K. Rowling (Bloomsbury) and the New Witches Club series by Debie Torkellson (Your Own World Books). Compare the styles of the two authors. Ask the children to select a particular part and tell a friend about it and why they like it. Encourage them to use language to persuade others how good it is. Ask the children to write a review of one of the books, and to read other books by the same author and create a reading journal.

- Act out a lesson at Harry Potter's school involving a 'change', such as a spell, or a scene from other literature involving witches or wizards, such as the three witches scene from Macbeth. Develop a group chant for accompaniment. Link with music and PE or dance.

- Find out about volcanoes. Ask, 'Which in the world are active now?' Ask the children to examine visual reports, make notes and write a report of an event. Develop into writing – prose or poems with several verses – which includes appearance, movement, feelings of people, effect on the environment and animals and so on.

- Carry out and report a 'Which' style report on a variety of biscuits or bread.

- Use the activity sheet on page 31 to focus the children's attention on good report writing.

Speaking and Listening

- Examine big chunks of ice in detail. Pretend they have broken off from the frozen sea at the North Pole. Discuss why this could be a problem. Link to global warming.

- Interview people involved with cooking, such as school cook, restaurant manager, parent or fast food worker. Ask the children to think of a selection of similar questions for each of them. After the interviews ask the children to compare the responses. Alternatively, interview a fireman about his work.

- Get the children to act each of the 'changes' studied. Can others guess which change they are portraying? Sequence the actions to show the changes involved in cleaning dirty water.

Be a teacher!

This is a piece of writing that Jojo did about his science enquiry.

> *Will all licwids freeze in the freezer?*
>
> This is what we want to find out. First We chose our licwids they were tomarto kechup vinegar washing up licwid milk oil and treekle. Jack said that treekle is not a licwid but i think it is so we used it anyway we needed to plan what do so we did and this is what we did.
>
> We used the same size plastick cups for all of them and dicided to put in 20ml of each and then we put them in the freezer we did it in the morning and loocked at them at lunchtime and when we went home than the next morning and lunchtime and when we went home we used water to becuase we kno that water freezes in the freezer because we did it before it was our prediction that they woud all freeze Do you no what we found out that tomato kechup did not freeze and we thaught it would of but it didn't. the water did and so did the vineger and the washing up licwid some of them were slow to freeze but they maniged it in the end.

Jojo has a problem with some spelling and punctuation. Some of the words are wrong too.

Be a teacher and correct his work.

Show a partner your corrections.

Do you both agree?

Which words would you put on Jojo's spelling list for him to learn?

Spelling list

He hasn't written his enquiry very clearly.

How much has he told you? What information is missing? Is it in the right order?

Can you write it out more clearly? Think about the scientific vocabulary you could use.

Carry out this enquiry at home or at school. Think of an interesting and clear way you could share your information with others.

BURN CANDLE BURN!

Maths

Using and Applying

● Estimate and time how long a candle takes to burn away. Change time units to seconds/minutes/hours. Calculate in fractions and decimal fractions. Make similar calculations using the activity sheet on page 33.

Measuring

● Measure the mass and volume of a range of candles. To measure volume, wrap paper around the candle to copy its shape, fill the paper roll with rice and pour into a measuring cylinder. Estimate how long each will burn for and what mass and volume would be left. Burn the candle. Observe the smoke emitted and changes in shape. When completed, re-measure. Discuss that if melting alone was occurring, the mass would be similar. Where has the extra mass gone? Explain that there is the irreversible change of burning occurring as well as melting. Gas is released in the smoke, so mass is lost. Display the calculations and observations as shown.

● Measure the volume of water before and after freezing. How has it changed — in appearance and/or measurements? Weigh and measure the volume/dimensions before and after. Ask the children to make up a generalisation based on their observations, such as 'water expands on freezing', 'the mass stays the same when water freezes'. They should test their idea on at least three volumes/masses to find out if it is true. Discuss why the test should be repeated several times. Different groups could try different volumes of water to save time!

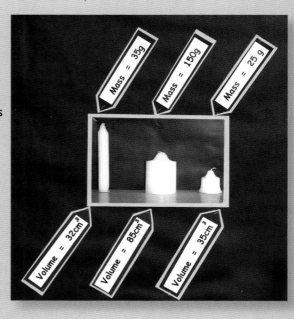

● Collect pebbles of all different sizes and shapes. Weigh them and convert the grams to kilograms. Measure their volume by displacement. Put water into a measuring cylinder and mark the level. Drop in a pebble so that it sinks. It displaces a volume of water equivalent to its volume. Read the new measurement of the new water level. Subtract the original level from the new level to give the volume of the pebble. Try other objects in this way. Can children suggest how to measure the volume of something that floats (like a candle)?

Reversible and Irreversible Change

Burning questions!

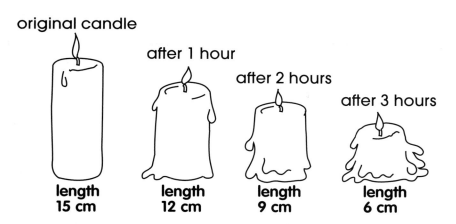

original candle

after 1 hour

after 2 hours

after 3 hours

length
15 cm

length
12 cm

length
9 cm

length
6 cm

The height of the candle above was measured as it burned away. Using the measurements, fill in the table below.

	Height after 1 hour	Height after 2 hours	Height after 3 hours
Fraction of original candle			
Decimal fraction of original candle			
Percentage of original candle			

How long will it take for all the candle to burn away? _____

NOW!

Here is a candle of a different size.

Draw a table like the one above on a separate piece of paper. Work out the fractions and percentages using the heights of these candles.

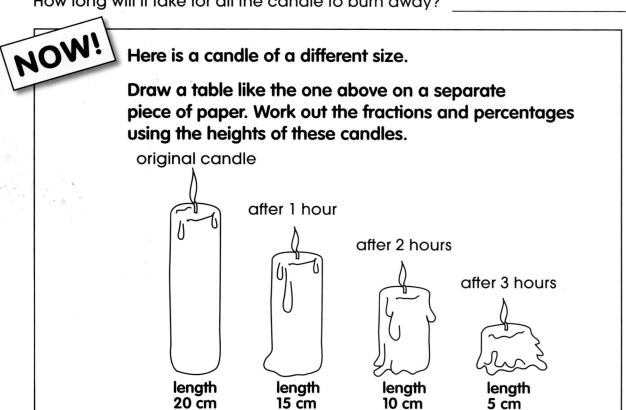

original candle

after 1 hour

after 2 hours

after 3 hours

length
20 cm

length
15 cm

length
10 cm

length
5 cm

Design & Technology

- Make a fizzy rocket that works using a chemical reaction between an antacid tablet and water. Use a film canister for the body with the lid as the stable base. Add a nosecone and fins made of thin card or plastic. Find a safe place with a high ceiling. Fill a quarter of the canister with water and add an antacid tablet. Stand well back. Try different liquids with the children, such as lemon juice or vinegar, and different amounts of tablet (a quarter, a half or a whole) to find out which is the best combination. The same method works to create a model of an active volcano.

Art

- Discuss the reasons why we need to recycle and re-use plastic bags. Use plastic bags to design clothes or accessories as on the display. Cut the plastic into strips and weave, plait, fold or scrunch a range of colours. Find ways to change the texture. Hold a fashion display of the results.

PSHCE

- Talk about manufactured materials that give off poisonous fumes when burned. Actates, nylon, polyesters and acrylic materials can drip when burned and all give off some dangerous fumes. Look at the following website, which gives brief and clear information: www.griffindyeworks.com/faqs/burntest.html. Talk about the dangers of burning these materials.

- Discuss how people are causing pollution. Which types of pollution can be reversed and which not? Devise strategies to solve environmental problems caused by people.

PE

- Use different stimuli for dance, such as *The firebird* by Igor Stravinsky (1882–1971) (based on a Russian fairy tale) and *Fire drums* by Ariel Kalma (b. 1938). Ask the children to listen and make movements on the spot before using the space around. Develop into pair and group work.

Music

- Listen to changing sounds, such as a sequence of humming, and represent each sound in the sequence with a drawn sign or symbol. Share sounds and ideas on the signs or symbols. Use signs to represent different volumes and pitch – use the activity sheet on page 35.

Changing Music

This is Joe and Becky's music to accompany a fairy tale which they wrote together.

Chapter 1

Chapter 2

Chapter 3

Can you play their music?

Work in a group and decide what each symbol means and how it might sound. Can you work out how they show changes in sound and pitch?

What will you use to make each sound? (You could use an instrument, other materials or your voices.)

Put the sounds together.

NOW!

Make up a fairytale of your own and write your own sounds to acompany it.

Forces in Action

These grids demonstrate the learning objectives covered in the activities within the theme. The curriculum references indicate the relevant programme of study (PoS) for a subject area unless otherwise stated.

	Learning Objectives	Curriculum References
Science (Page 38)		
Scientific Enquiry	Make repeated measurements of force.	Sc1/2e-j; Sc4/2e
	Use scientific knowledge to explain results.	Sc1/2l
	Carry out complete investigations, recognising factors to change and keep the same to make fair comparisons.	Sc1/2a-m
Physical Processes (QCA Science Unit 6E)	Name different forces acting on moving objects.	Sc4/2b-c
	Recognise that forces can cause objects to speed up, slow down or change directions.	Sc4/2c
	Compare the size of force in newtons.	Sc4/2e
	Represent the direction of force by arrows.	Sc4/2e
	Know that gravity is the result of the Earth and objects pulling towards each other.	Sc4/2b
Life Processes and Living Things	Name bones in the body and how they work with muscles for movement (see PSHCE).	Sc2/2e
	Know the purpose of joints in the body (see PSHCE).	Sc2/2e
Literacy (Page 40)		
Speaking	Discuss why we wear shoes.	En1/1a;3a
Listening and Responding	Present information about the Olympic Games (or other sports events) past and present.	En1/1a-f;2a-e
Understanding and Interpreting Texts	Find out about famous sportspeople.	En2/3a-f;5a,c,d,e,f
	Read stories/myths and legends of ancient Greece.	En2/4a-f;8b,e,f
Creating and Shaping Texts	Make up Haiku about sports.	En3/1a-e;2a-f;12
	Describe shoes.	En3/1a-e;2a-f;9a
Mathematics (Page 42)		
Using and Applying Mathematics	Identify mathematics used in different sports.	Ma2/1a,c,e,f,i;Ma3/1a-f
Understanding Shape	Investigate kite shapes.	Ma3/2a-c;4e
	Draw coordinates of shapes on grids in different quadrants.	Ma3/2a-c;3a-c
	Rotate and reflect shapes on grids.	Ma3/2a-c;3a-c
Measuring	Measure distance, weight and time accurately.	Ma3/1a;4a-d
	Measure angles and perimeters of mathematical shapes.	Ma3/1a;2a-c;4a-d
Handling Data	Use spreadsheets to analyse data of science enquiries.	Ma3/1a;2a,f; QCA ICT Units 5D & 6B

Forces in Action

Learning Objectives	Curriculum References
Design Technology (Page 44)	
Make kites.	PoS 1a-d;2a-e;3a-c;4a;5a-c
Construct marble runs.	PoS 1a-d;2a-e;3a-e;4a;5a-c
PSHCE (Page 44)	
Know that exercise is important for health.	Sc2/2h; PSHCE PoS 3a
Debate the pros and cons of large sporting events.	PoS 2a,b,e,f,g,j,k;4a,b,d,e,f
Compare communities in the world who take part in sporting events.	PoS 1a,b;2e,i;4a,b,e,f;5a,b,c,e,f,g; QCA Citizenship Unit 05
Geography (Page 44)	
Identify countries on a globe and map.	PoS 2a,c
Plan a journey to a sports event.	PoS 1a-e;2a-g;3b,c,f,g; QCA Geography Units 18 & 24
Describe places and the people there.	PoS 1a-e;2a-g;3b,c,f,g; QCA Geography Unit 24; QCA Citizenship Unit 5
PE (Page 44)	
Hold a skills event and complete various activities in one minute.	PoS 1a,b
Play bat and ball games.	PoS 1a,b;2a-c;3a,b;7a-c; QCA PE Units 32 & 24
Devise own games and rules.	PoS 1a,b;2a-c;7a-c; QCA PE Units 32 & 24
Find format and rules of games that use balls.	PoS 1a,b;2a-c
History (Page 45)	
Find out about Isaac Newton and his work on forces.	PoS 2a;4a;5a
Compare lives and sports in ancient Greece with those today.	PoS 1a,b;2a,c;4a,b;5a-c; QCA History Unit 14
Devise a multi-media presentation about the Greeks/Olympic Games.	PoS 1a,b;2a-d;3;4a,b;5a; QCA History Unit 15; QCA ICT Unit 6A
Art (Page 45)	
Make up a group/class display of a Greek legend.	PoS 1a-c;2a-c;3a,b;4a;5a,b
Make up own impressions of storms.	PoS 1a-c;2a-c;3a,b;4a;5a-c
Music (Page 45)	
Devise stormy music.	PoS 1b,c;2a,b;3a-c;4a-d;5a-e; QCA Music Unit 21
Devise music for the Sirens who lure Odysseus.	PoS 1b,c;2a,b;3a-c;4a-d;5a-e; QCA Music Unit 21
MFL (Page 45)	
Identify different parts of the body and sports.	PoS 1a-c;3a; QCA MFL Unit 9
Ask and answer questions about sports.	PoS 1a-d;2a,b;3a,b,c,e,f,g; QCA MFL Unit 9
Talk about a sport.	PoS 1a-d;2a,b;3a,b,c,e,f,g; QCA MFL Unit 9

Forces in Action

Starting Points

- Find out what the children remember about forces by carrying out simple activities to demonstrate different forces in action. You could have a context, such as sports activities, and display the names of forces and direction on a display as shown. Sport suggestions:

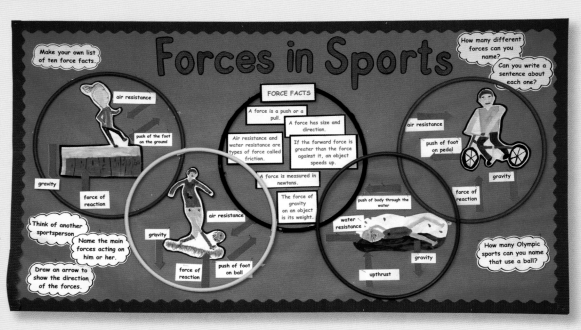

- for air resistance show a person cycling, a parachute falling
- for water resistance show a person and boat moving through water
- for friction on land show a cyclist again, or a runner.

Explain that gravity is one force always present which is balanced by a force upwards – the force of reaction or upthrust in water.

- Remind the children that a force is a push or a pull and has direction. Ask them to think of other sports activities of their own and identify the main forces (e.g. weightlifter, footballer, cricketer).

Enquiry

- As gravity is always acting on objects on Earth, and children often have some misconceptions about it, the following enquiry helps by focusing on falling things. Ask the children, *'What might make a difference to how quickly things fall?'* Ideas could include, shape, mass weight, shininess, how stiff it is, etc. To focus on shape, drop a flat sheet of A4 paper, then one folded in half and another screwed up into a ball. Predict, then compare, the rates at which they fall to find that shape does make a difference.

- Ask, *'Does mass make a difference to how quickly things fall?'* Discuss factors that need to be kept constant for a fair test. To keep the shape the same use film canisters or similar coins. Drop an empty film canister and one filled with Plasticine at the same time, from the same height. Observe that they land at the same time. Try other masses of similar shape and different masses. Make a generalisation: 'Objects of the same shape and different mass fall at the same rate.'

Extension Activities

- Look at a range of force meters. Use them to open doors, pull objects, weigh objects in water and the air. Discuss how the meters work. Compare force meters used to measure different sizes of forces.

- Consider the forces acting on objects in water. Using the activity sheet on page 38 the children can compare the rate of fall of sinking objects through liquids with different viscosities.

Things falling through liquids

Isla and George put all these things in water. What do you think will happen?

Test them to find out if you are right. Write your results in the correct bubble below.

These things sink:

These things float:

Isla and George wanted to find out if the objects that sank would sink in the same way in different liquids. Test how long it takes the objects to sink in water and fill in the table below.

In water		
object	prediction	time

On a separate sheet of paper draw tables for washing-up liquid and oil. Test the objects in each liquid and fill in the tables.

NOW! In which liquid would it be the easiest to swim? Use scientific vocabulary of force, friction and water resistance to explain why.

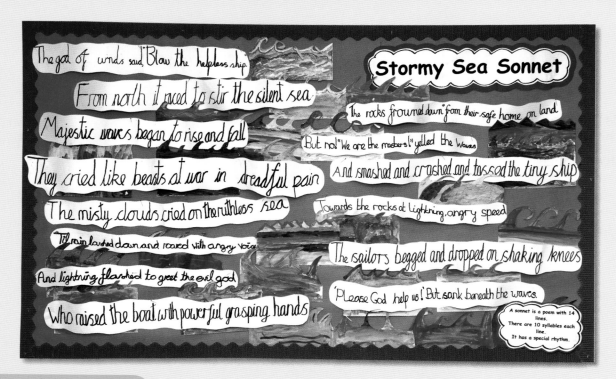

The god of winds said "Blow the helpless ship"
From north it raced to stir the silent sea.
Majestic waves began to rise and fall
They cried like beasts at war in dreadful pain
The misty clouds cried on the ruthless sea
Til rain lashed down and roared with angry voice
And lightning flashed to greet the evil god
Who raised the boat with powerful grasping hands

Stormy Sea Sonnet

The rocks frowned down from their safe home on land
But no! "We are the masters!" yelled the waves
And smashed and crashed and tossed the tiny ship
Towards the rocks at lightning, angry speed
The sailors begged and dropped on shaking knees
'Please God help us!' But sank beneath the waves.

A sonnet is a poem with 14 lines.
There are 10 syllables each line.
It has a special rhythm.

Literacy

Reading and Writing

● Discuss sonnets and their format – 14 lines, each line has 10 syllables with an iambic meter – for example: we ASK you TO forGIVE us ALL our SINS. Compose a group sonnet that uses the theme of force (e.g. in the context of sports, myths and legends or natural phenomena involving forces). The display above is based around the journey of Odysseus. Sonnets traditionally have a rhyming pattern but children are likely to find it difficult to both tell the story and use rhyme as well at this stage. Focus on the use of language in telling the story, explaining that, 'Poetry is the best words in the best order'. The activity sheet on page 41 has the bones of a sonnet but does not obey the rules. Pairs of children take each line and extend it to 10 syllables with the right pattern before assembling it as a whole. This method was used to write the 'Stormy Sea' sonnet in the display.

● Compose haiku about different sportspeople in action. For example:

The long jumper sprints	The rower pulls hard	The swimmer glides past
Like a rocket taking off	Against the dragging water	Apparently effortless
Kicking legs, then lands	Gulping in fresh air	Just like an arrow

For a variety of poetic forms see *A kick in the head: an everyday guide to poetic forms* by Paul B. Janeczko (Walker Books).

● Read *The adventures of Odysseus* by Hugh Lupton and Daniel Morden (Barefoot, 2006). Identify the forces he had to deal with. Ask the children to write one of his adventures from his point of view or the viewpoint of one of his crew. Encourage the children to make up a play that tells the story. Read other myths and legends involving forces, such as: Icarus and Daedalus, with Icarus flying too near to the Sun.

● Find out about the ancient Olympic Games – the sports, rewards, contestants, arenas, etc. Compare with the modern Olympic games. Make a multi-media presentation about the Olympic Games or other sports events.

Speaking and Listening

● Choose a particular sportsperson. Find out ten facts about him or her. Can others guess who it is from the facts presented?

● Discuss answers to: 'Why do we wear shoes?' Ask the children to write a description of, e.g. 'the coolest/most beautiful/ballerina's shoe', using as many senses as possible – their appearance, the sounds they make, their 'smelliness', materials used to make them, and their usefulness. Ask the children to make up a radio, TV or poster advertisement for the best sports shoe ever.

Sonny's sonnet

This is the story of a football match. Sonny is so excited that he has written a sonnet to tell everyone what happened. He has written 14 lines but it does not have the right number of syllables or the correct rhythm. Can you change each line so it has 10 syllables and the correct de-dum rhythm?

Here's an example for a first line:

The **ma**nager has **chos**en me to**day** or
The **ma**nager has **picked** me **for** the **match**

Both of these lines have 10 syllables. Say the lines out loud so you get the idea of the pattern.

Now change each line to make the same pattern.

You could change the ending so that he misses the goal!

The manager has picked me

It's the first time

It's so exciting to wear the kit

And jog onto the pitch

The opposition wear their kit

It seems there's twenty of them

The whistle goes, my heart starts to race

My legs start running

Oh no! the ball is at my feet

No-one to pass to

Defenders crowd around

Legs come out to tackle

Still I go on dribbling

I shoot and score a goal!

When you have finished your poem, read it aloud to a friend. Now try to improve it by using some more interesting words.

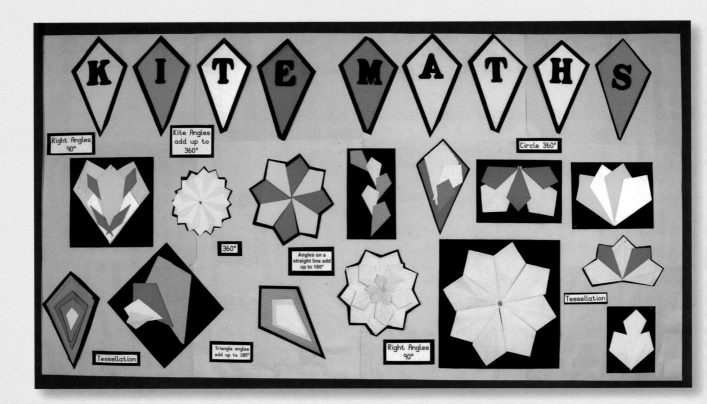

Maths

Understanding Shape

- Calculate then measure angles in regular kite shapes using the activity sheet on page 43. Make up kites to this pattern. Look at other designs for kites and measure the angles on them. Use to create a variety of patterns as shown in the display.

- Make a kite shape on a grid. Write the coordinates, then rotate and reflect the same shape in different quadrants and identify the new coordinates. Do the same for other shapes.

Using and Applying

- List five different sports or hobbies. Ask groups to select one and list at least three ways in which maths is involved in the activity.

  - For a sport, the following could be included: playing areas; measurements of time, height and width; shapes of equipment; cost of kit, etc. Ask them to present their information to other groups as a multi-media presentation. Link to ICT.

  - For another hobby, such as chess, dancing, climbing, camping, sewing, orienteering, the following could be included: measurements of areas and time; cost of equipment, clothes; direction etc.

Measuring

- Calculate averages and mean times of three or five sets in a tennis match. Make up questions about data.

- Throw a variety of balls, under-arm and over-arm, and to measure the distances they travel. Compare distances – Is there a pattern between mass or size of ball and distance thrown? Ask them to present their results and ask: 'Why is it important to repeat the activity several times?'

- Ask groups to find out how much force the children can push with their legs. Lean some bathroom scales upright against a wall. Ask children to sit on the floor and press the scales as hard as possible with a foot. Another child can take the reading. Take turns and compare the results.

- Make spreadsheets of data collected in science enquiries such as:
  - How does the size of a parachute affect how long it takes to land?
  - How does the height you drop a ball from affect how high it bounces?

Forces in Action

Let's fly a kite!

Next to each letter write the size of the angle in degrees.
Predict the size of each of the angles on the next two kites.
Measure to check.

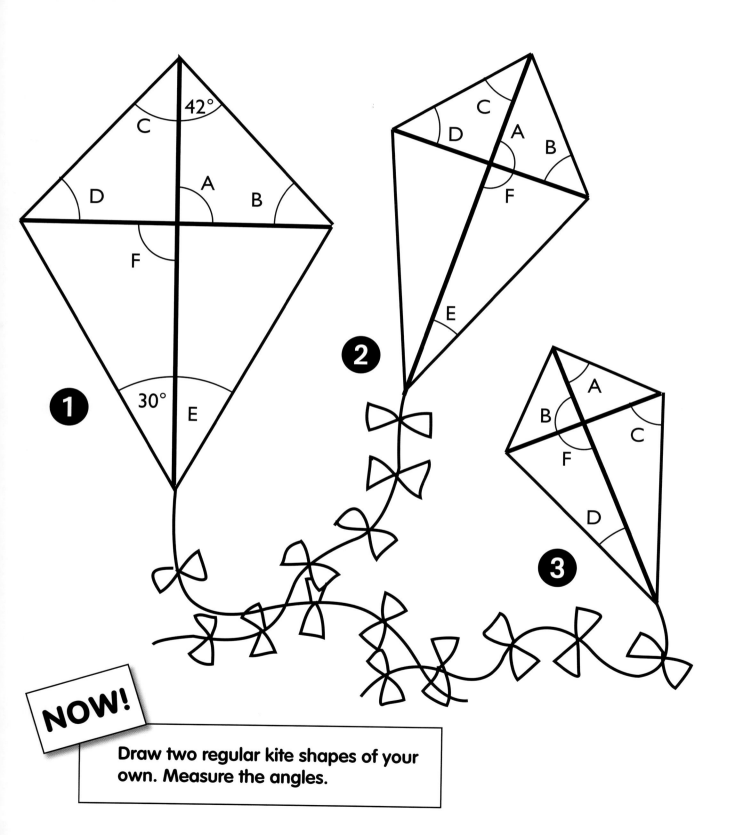

Design & Technology

- Fly a plastic bag kite on a stick. Talk about the forces in action whilst flying a kite. Make simple kite shapes to fly, e.g. join paper plates together like a dragon and fly them from a stick. Link with kite festivals all over the world or create a themed kite display (see above).

- Construct a marble run from card. Can the children make it so that the marble takes one minute from start to finish? Talk about the forces acting on it. Discuss when it is good to have a lot of friction (running, playing football) and when not (sledging, ice skating).

PSHCE

- Review the names of the parts of bodies and bones involved in different movements. Revise how muscles and joints help us to move and the benefits of exercise. Link with MFL (see page 45).

- What are the advantages and disadvantages of big international sports events? Debate whether they should continue or not.

Geography

- Find out which nations take part in an Olympic Games or in another international games. Identify the countries on a globe and find their flags. Write a leaflet about the country, either to advertise it or to present country details to the Olympic committee. Ask the children to write the information as a fax or email.

- Plan a journey from a selected country's team to the Olympic Games or to another event. Ask the children to decide how they will get there, the costs and the time the journey will take. Make comparisons between the team's country and the location of the Games (e.g. compare currency, landscape, weather, customs, culture, religion).

PE

- Hold a skills event entitled 'How many … can you do in a minute?' Estimate one minute in time.
  Activities could include bouncing a ball, skipping with a rope forwards/backwards, scoring a goal in netball or basketball, etc.

- Play games with a bat and ball. Identify where the forces are acting. How far can children hit/throw a ball? Make up a game with a bat and ball. List Olympic games that use a ball.

Forces in Action

History

- Ask the children to find out what events were in the original pentathlon, the athletics pentathlon today and the modern pentathlon. Ask them to gather information about the individual sports and make a multimedia presentation that includes text, sound and images.
- Find out about Isaac Newton (1642–1727) and his work on forces.

Art

- Create displays of a Greek myth or legend, such as the journey of Odysseus and the sirens as on the display shown. Link with Music.
- Look at pictures that depict great activity/movement, e.g. stormy seas or stormy weather. Look at pictures by different artists representing the same theme and compare with, for example, real stormy skies and rain. Ask the children to create their own picture of stormy skies. Remind them to select colours and shapes to depict an impression of a storm.

Music

- Devise music for a Greek myth or legend – for example represent some of the story of Odysseus and his journey, such as the song of the Sirens and stormy seas. Link with Literacy and accompany the music with readings from poems or stories.

MFL

- Cut out the head of a famous sportsperson and draw a body underneath. Ask the children to label the drawing in the language studied. Practise pronunciation. Write and ask questions and answers about the sportsperson.

How We See Things

These grids demonstrate the learning objectives covered in the activities within the theme. The curriculum references indicate the relevant programme of study (PoS) for a subject area unless otherwise stated.

	Learning Objectives	Curriculum References
Science (Page 48)		
Scientific Enquiry	Find out how light is reflected.	Sc1/e-m
	Use examples to explain how scientists work.	Sc1/1a
Physical Processes (QCA Science Unit 6F)	Know that light travels from a source.	Sc4/3a
	Know that we see things because light from them enters the eye.	Sc4/3d
	Know that shiny things reflect light better than dull ones.	Sc4/c
	Understand how we see shadows.	Sc4/3b
	Understand the difference between shadows and reflections.	Sc4/3b,d
	Recognise properties of materials.	Sc3/1a; ICT PoS1a-c
Literacy (Page 50)		
Speaking/Group Discussion	Argue a global/local issue, explaining viewpoint.	En1/3a-e
Drama	Present own version of Aladdin.	En1/4a-d
	Devise a script about wishes.	En1/4a-d
Engaging With and Responding to Texts	Read about a famous blind person.	En2/3a-c
	List phrases about seeing and eyes and their meanings.	En2/4a
	Use a familiar phrase about seeing to inform writing.	En3/1a-e;2a-f
	Read about myths and legends about reflections (Narcissus, Perseus and Medusa).	En2/2a-d;4a-e
Creating and Shaping Texts	Make up wanted posters for a character.	En3/1a-e
	Make up stories about Aladdin's lamp and wishes.	En3/1a-e;2a-f
Mathematics (Page 52)		
Understanding Shape	Draw symmetrical 2-D shapes on grids.	Ma2/2c
	Identify lines of symmetry.	Ma2/2c
	Rotate shapes in different quadrants.	Ma2/3a-c
Measuring	Calculate perimeters and areas of shapes.	Ma2/4e
	Estimate and measure angles in 2-D shapes.	Ma2/4b,c

Learning Objectives	Curriculum References
PSHCE (Page 54)	
Find out about rules of the road and who is responsible for them.	PoS 1a-c;2a,b,c,g;3f;4a,d;5a,b,c,e,g,h ; QCA Citizenship Unit 08
To discuss the need for rules and laws.	PoS 1a;2b;3f; QCA Citizenship Unit 08
History (Page 54)	
Compare places locally with how they were in the past.	PoS 4a,b;5a
Find out about the lives of Thomas Edison and Logie Baird and what they tell us about the times when they lived.	PoS 1a,b;2a,c,d;3;4a,b; QCA History Unit 12; QCA ICT Unit 6D
Find out about discoveries in the past about light and how we use it in everyday life.	PoS 1a,b;2a-d;3;4a,b; QCA History Unit 12; QCA ICT Unit 6D
Design & Technology (Page 54)	
Make a kaleidoscope and a zoetrope.	PoS 2d,e
Create a shadow or hand puppet show.	PoS 1a-d;2a-e;3a-c;4a
Make traffic lights.	PoS 1a-d;2a-e;3a-c;4a,c,d; QCA ICT Unit 6C
Art (Page 55)	
Represent the environment in different media.	PoS 1a-c;2a-c;3a,b;4a,b;5a; QCA Art Unit 6C
Explore the work of a variety of artists and copying the style.	PoS 4c; QCA ICT Unit 5A
Explore colour and shades in developing own style.	PoS 1a-c;2a-c;3a,b;4a,b;5a
Geography (Page 55)	
Identify local places from photographs taken at odd angles.	PoS 1c;2b-d;3a-d
Find out about festivals of light in the world.	PoS 1b,c;2a-d;3e,f; QCA Geography Unit 24
Music (Page 55)	
Listen to and learn colour songs.	PoS 1a,c
Compose own verse and chorus to give a message/describe colour.	PoS 1a-c;2a,b
RE (Page 55)	
Find out about religious festivals of light for different faiths.	PoS 1a,b,e;2a
MFL (Page 55)	
Describe presents at festivals.	PoS 1a-g;2a,b

How We See Things

Science

Starting Points

- Discuss how shiny objects reflect more light than dull ones which absorb a lot of light.

- Read the story of Perseus and his slaying of Medusa. Draw diagrams to show how he saw her in his shiny shield as on the display (right). This will highlight any misconceptions children have about how light travels from a source to a shiny object where it is reflected into the eye.

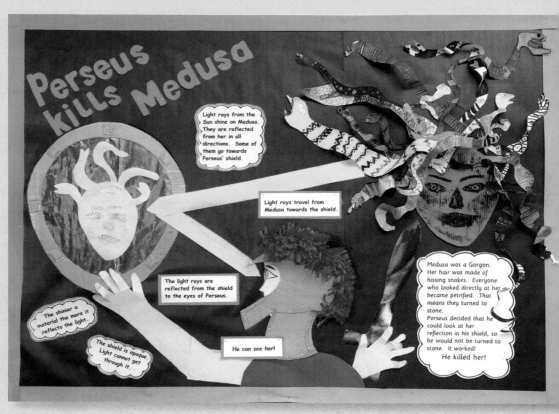

Enquiry

- Mark a chalk line along the floor at right angles to a wall.

  - Roll a ball along the ground towards where the chalk line meets the wall. Note the direction of travel before and after it hits the wall. Try rolling the ball at different angles to the wall. Measure the angles as shown here.

  - Now repeat using light rays from a torch to a mirror instead of the wall. It is best if the room is dark. Measure the angles of the torch, as with the ball. Both angles should be the same. Draw a diagram using arrows to represent the light beam.

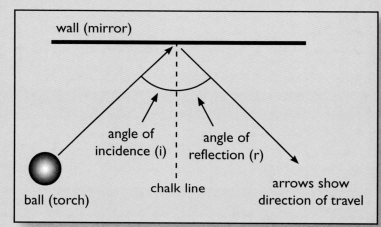

Extension Activities

- Play with two mirrors. Put them at different angles to each other and different distances. Observe and record how the light form a torch is reflected. Look for patterns. Draw the light rays with arrows to show how they see each reflection. Try more than two mirrors. Challenge children to find a way to make a light ray from a torch get to a specific point. Set challenges: Can you see round a corner? Under the chair? Behind you? Link to how we use mirrors everyday (e.g. car mirrors, dentists, periscopes, changing-room mirrors in shops).

- Make shadows and draw light rays to show how shadows are made. Compare this with how reflections are made. Both are made when light rays hit an object. If the object is opaque, some light bounces off it (reflects); the rest is absorbed by the object, so none gets through (creates a shadow). Use the activity sheet on page 49 to focus on shadows.

Spot the mistakes

Tick the box that shows the shadow in the correct place.
Underneath each one write what is wrong or right about it.

NOW!

Write instructions on how to make a shadow:

• How We See Things • Belair Curricular-Links Science 6

Literacy

Speaking and Listening

- Devise imaginary wanted posters for a character who has committed a crime. Find out from the police the information to put on the posters. Explore the character of the person. Link with numeracy when drawing faces on grids. One child could present their poster to the class as if they were a policeman, while the class takes notes about the wanted character. Ask questions in role. How effective are the posters at making people read them? Display the posters as shown.

Reading and Writing

- Show an old lamp to the children and explain that it is magic, like Aladdin's lamp. Ask them to imagine that when they rub it a genie appears from inside and offers to grant them a wish. Would their eyes pop out of their heads? Ask them to invent and write about their own lamp. Where would it be kept? What would its genie look like? What would they wish for? Use the activity sheet on page 51 as a starting point.

- Read myths and legends about light, e.g. the Norse myth of how Odin lost his eye or the Greek myth of how Narcissus fell in love with his reflection. Encourage the children to devise a modern play about light, shadows or reflections.

- Parents and teachers have eyes in the backs of their heads, so they say! Discuss the things they might see out the backs of their heads, e.g. 'This eye tells about things that might go unnoticed and are unlikely to happen or impossible to see with two eyes. This eye knows the truth.' Write a story/poem about their ideas.

- Use a familiar colloquialism about seeing to inspire the children's writing, e.g. Seeing is believing! An eye for an eye! In the public eye! Keep one's eyes open! See you later!

- Read about famous blind people in different walks of life, such as Helen Keller (1880–1868) (blind and deaf); Thomas Rhodes Armitage (1824–1890) who founded the RNIB; Louis Braille (1809–1852); Ray Charles (1930–2004), Stevie Wonder (b.1950) and Andrea Bocelli (b.1958) (singers); John Milton (1608–1674) (English poet); Samson and St Paul (in the Bible); Homer (750–650 BCE) (Greek poet); Odin and Cupid (ancient gods); Horatio Nelson (1758–1805) (British sailor). Produce a leaflet about the life and achievements of one of them. Link with history (people from the past).

How We See Things

Three Wishes

What three wishes will you make? Why?

WISH 1

WISH 2

WISH 3

NOW!

Choose one of your wishes. What happens next? Write your ideas on another sheet of paper.

Maths

Understanding Shape

- Revise lines of symmetry by writing letters in upper and lower case and drawing in lines of symmetry. Sort into those that have none, one and more than one line of symmetry. Look at letters in a mirror held at the side and then above. Which ones look the same? Ask the children to try to copy some reflective writing. Can anyone read it?

- Draw a simple shape on a grid towards the centre. Draw the same shape twice 3 and 4 times as big and as small. Write the coordinates of at least the same 3 points on the shape at each stage. Look for the patterns in the coordinates. See the 'multiplication man' opposite.

- Revise reflective symmetry and coordinates in two quadrants – draw half a face or other shape on a grid and ask children to complete it so that it is symmetrical. Ask more able children to write the coordinates for each point. A similar activity is provided on the activity sheet on page 53.

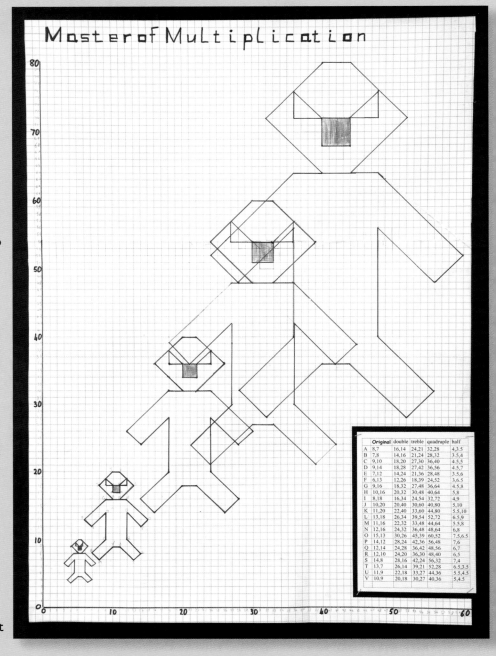

Master of Multiplication

	Original	double	treble	quadruple	half
A	8,7	16,14	24,21	32,28	4,3.5
B	7,8	14,16	21,24	28,32	3.5,4
C	9,10	18,20	27,30	36,40	4.5,5
D	9,14	18,28	27,42	36,56	4.5,7
E	7,12	14,24	21,36	28,48	3.5,6
F	6,13	12,26	18,39	24,52	3,6.5
G	9,16	18,32	27,48	36,64	4.5,8
H	10,16	20,32	30,48	40,64	5,8
I	8,18	16,34	24,54	32,72	4,9
J	10,20	20,40	30,60	40,80	5,10
K	11,20	22,40	33,60	44,80	5.5,10
L	13,18	26,34	39,54	52,72	6.5,9
M	11,16	22,32	33,48	44,64	5.5,8
N	12,16	24,32	36,48	48,64	6,8
O	15,13	30,26	45,39	60,52	7.5,6.5
P	14,12	28,24	42,36	56,48	7,6
Q	12,14	24,28	36,42	48,56	6,7
R	12,10	24,20	36,30	48,40	6,5
S	14,8	28,16	42,24	56,32	7,4
T	13,7	26,14	39,21	52,28	6.5,3.5
U	11,9	22,18	33,27	44,36	5.5,4.5
V	10,9	20,18	30,27	40,36	5,4.5

Measuring

- Measure the angles of light rays made when shining a beam into a mirror (the angle of incidence and angle of reflection). Link to science – see page 48.

- Calculate the perimeters and areas of the shapes drawn in the activities above by measuring the perimeters and counting squares for the areas.

- Make circular colour wheels. Split a circle into six equal areas. Colour in alternate areas in the primary colours – red, blue and yellow. Mix the two colours either side of it to fill in the other three areas. The wheel now has six colours of the rainbow. Calculate and check the sizes of the six areas by measuring the degrees of each area at the centre. Revise the total number of degrees at the centre of a circle. Ask the children how many lines of symmetry the shape has?

- Place the colour wheel from the above activity on a spindle of an electric motor and spin to see what happens to the colours. Repeat with circles that have different angles at the centre and different colours. Keep a record of the colours seen. If the wheel spins quickly enough and the colours are pure, they will blend to make white. Usually they blend into a greyish colour.

How We See Things

Let's face it!

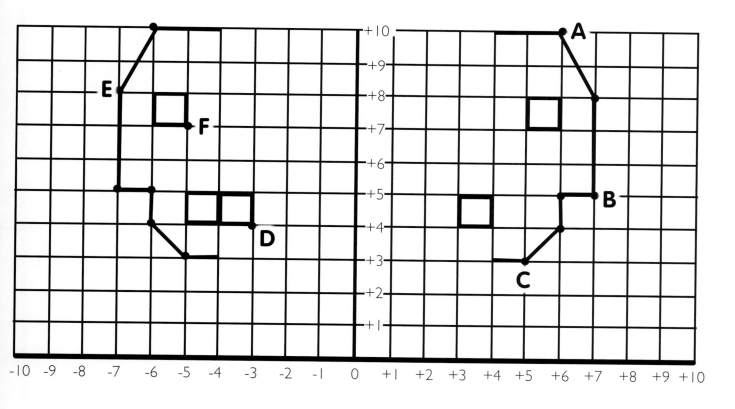

Complete each face so that it is symmetrical and both are the same. What are the coordinates of points

A ....   B ....

C ....   D ....

E ....   F ....

NOW!

Make up a shape of your own on another piece of squared paper and draw its reflection.

Put in the coordinates where you can.

PSHCE

- Discuss why road signs are needed and who is responsible for them. Which colours are used in them? Which combinations show up best in the day and at night?

- Learn the sequence of traffic lights. Make model traffic lights and attach to a computer. Link with ICT.

- Find out about lantern festivals in different parts of the world. Research their significance. The children could organise a festival of their own.

History

- Visit a local library or contact the local council for information and old photos of the local area and compare with the same locations today. Select some buildings to sketch and put on a time line. Discuss important features to note, e.g. chimneys, doors and windows (blocked out windows, etc), brickwork, shape, etc. Select one aspect, such as chimneys, for each group to research. Ask them to put the buildings in time order. Consider the use of particular buildings now and in the past.

- Ask the children to research past discoveries about light and how it is used in everyday lives. Key figures are Humphrey Davy (1778–1829), Thomas Edison (1847–1931) and Logie Baird (1888–1946). What would life be like today without one of the inventions?

The further away things are, the smaller and fainter they look.

Design & Technology

- Show the children some manufactured kaleidoscopes and discuss how they work, using reflections in mirrors. It is easy to make one. Instructions can be found at the following website: http://kids.nationalgeographic.com/ Activities/FunScience.

- Design and make a zoetrope. A zoetrope was first made in 1830. It has separate pictures of on object in different positions inside a drum. When the drum is rotated, the object appears to move. For instructions, click on 'Things to do' on the following website: www.bbc.co.uk/ cbbc/bluepeter/

- Make backgrounds to illustrate that the further away things are, the smaller and fainter they appear. See the display above. It is useful to limit the colours to accentuate the point. Complete the scene by adding a foreground.

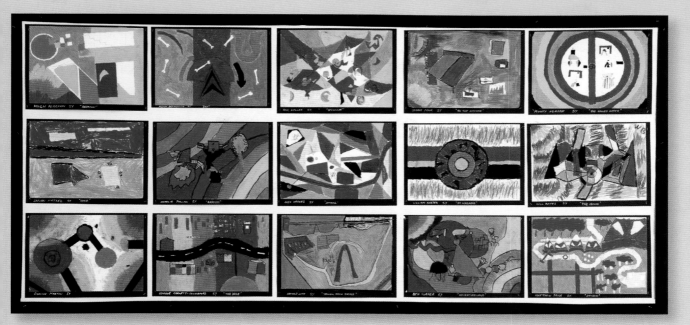

Art

- Look at abstract art by Picasso (1881–1973), Kandinsky (1866–1944), Damien Hirst (b.1965) etc. Ask the children to take some of these artists' ideas about feelings, colour, shape, pattern and composition to compose their own pictures like those on the Kandinsky-style display above. They could use a computer program to design their image. The following website allows children to compose their own Picasso-style picture: www.mrpicassohead.com.

- Look at how artists, such as J.M.W. Turner (1775–1851), portray skies and the sea – with the latter reflecting the colour of the sky. Ask the children to mix primary colours to depict them in a sunset, starting with pale blue and building up colour and shapes. Add a foreground with, for example, a boat, lighthouse or birds.

Geography

- Find out about light festivals in different countries of the world. Ask the children to mark the countries on a map and add photographs and pictures. Find out about the origins of the festivals. Most have them at different times, some are religious (link with RE) and others involve a tradition developed over centuries. Carry out a light festival on its special day, making artefacts and cloths to present it to others.

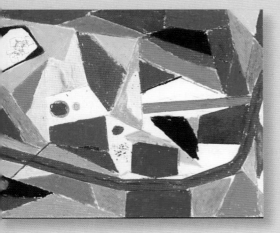

- Take photos of places in the locality or school at odd angles. The children must guess where they are. The children could take the photos themselves and use them in a quiz.

Music

- Listen to and learn colour songs, such as Any dream will do, from *Joseph and the amazing technicolor dreamcoat* and *I can sing a rainbow*.

- Select music to play alongside a hand-shadow puppet show (see DT activities on page 54).

RE

- Find out how light is used by different faiths in their festivals, e.g. Hanukkah, Diwali,

MFL

- Use festivals to revise the names of presents, colours, clothes and dates.

Changing Circuits

These grids demonstrate the learning objectives covered in the activities within the theme. The curriculum references indicate the relevant programme of study (PoS) for a subject area unless otherwise stated.

	Learning Objectives	Curriculum References
Science (Page 58)		
Scientific Enquiry	Carry out investigations into ways of changing circuits.	Sc1/2b-m; Sc3/2c
Physical Processes (QCA Science Unit 6G)	Make circuits with different components.	Sc4/1a
	Change the speed of motors, brightness of lamps, sound of buzzers.	Sc4/1b
	Use symbols for electrical components.	Sc4/1c
	Make circuit diagrams.	Sc4/1c
Literacy (Page 60)		
Speaking	Debate how electricity should be produced in the future.	En1/3a-d
Drama	Devise a play about electricity and safety.	En1/4a-d
Understanding and Interpreting Texts	Find out about the lives of scientists involved with the discovery of electricity.	En2/3a-e;5a-g
	Find out how electricity is made.	En2/3a-e;5a-g
Creating and Shaping Texts	Describe a character in an electrical story.	En3/7a-d;9a,b
	Describe a fairground/power station/ride on a fairground.	En3/7a-d;9a,b
	Make a list/poster of tips for saving electricity.	En3/1a-e;2a-f
	Instruct how to make an electric machine or toy/ how it works.	En3/1a-e;7b
Presentation	Design a poster about electrical safety.	En3/1a-e;7b
Mathematics (Page 62)		
Using and Applying Mathematics	Find out the best value for multiple packs of batteries.	Ma2/1a-i;3a,i;4a-c
	Read an electricity meter at different times and calculate the bill.	Ma2/1a-e;3a;4a-c
	Calculate electricity bills and suggest ways to reduce it.	Ma2/4a-c
	Calculate the cost of running appliances.	Ma2/1b,c,f,h,i; PoS ICT1a
Counting and Understanding Number	Use symbols in mathematics and know what they represent.	Ma2/1g,i;2c;4d
Handling Data	Draw graphs to show different types of information about electricity.	Ma4/2b,c,e,f
	Construct a pie chart to show different ways in which electricity is produced/where it is used in everyday life.	Ma4/2b,f
	Use a computer to make different types of graphs and charts.	Ma4/2c; PoS ICT3a

Changing Circuits

Learning Objectives	Curriculum References
Music (Page 64)	
Devise rounds and other types of songs about electricity.	PoS 1a;2a,b;3a,b; QCA Music Unit 17
Use musical instruments to represent the sound of electricity.	PoS 1b,c;2a,b;3a,b;4b-d
Devise symbols to represent their compositions.	PoS 4c
Design & Technology (Page 64)	
Construct fairground models.	PoS 1a-d;2a-e;3a-c;4a,b;5a QCA D & T Units 6C, 6D
Construct electrical models.	PoS 1a-d;2a-e;3a-c;4a,b;5a QCA D & T Units 6C, 6D
Art (Page 64)	
Design fairground art for models/pictures.	PoS 1a-c;2b,c;3a,b;4a-c
PSHCE (Page 65)	
Explain the uses and dangers of electricity.	PoS 3e,g
Evaluate electrical safety in the home.	PoS 3e,g
Devise rules for using electricity.	PoS 3e,g
Discuss ways in which we can save electricity and why it is important.	PoS 1a,c;2a,f,j;5d
Consider the importance of electricity in people's jobs and society.	PoS 1a,e;2a,b,d;5e-h; QCA Citizenship Unit 04
History (Page 65)	
Compare the lives of people before and after electricity (Victorians, Tudors, since 1948).	PoS 1a,b;2c;4a,b;11a,b; QCA History Units 11–13
Find out the development of uses of electricity from its discovery to the present.	PoS 1a,b;2a,b;3;4a,b;5a-c
Research inventors of electrical devices.	PoS 1a,b
Geography (Page 65)	
Investigate how people communicate places through fax, telephone and e-mail.	PoS 2d,f; QCA Geography Unit18
Discuss the place of TV and computers in the lives of people/children today.	PoS 2a,d,f
Discuss topical issues about electricity consumption – how it is produced and the alternatives.	PoS 5a,b
PE (Page 65)	
Use electrically produced music to stimulate dance.	PoS 6b; QCA PE Unit 22

Changing Circuits

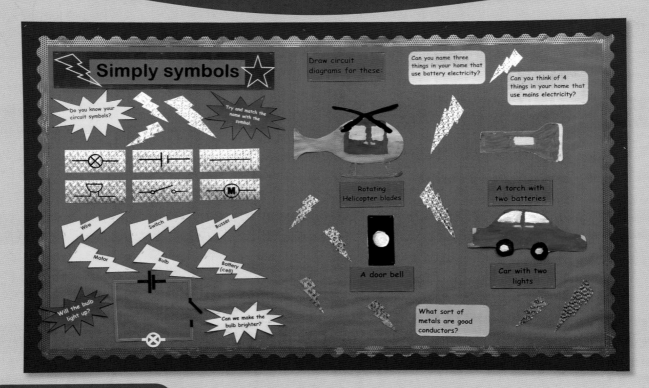

Science

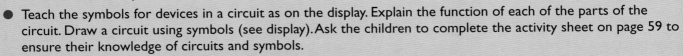

Starting Points

- Always begin a study of electricity with a discussion on safety.

- Teach the symbols for devices in a circuit as on the display. Explain the function of each of the parts of the circuit. Draw a circuit using symbols (see display). Ask the children to complete the activity sheet on page 59 to ensure their knowledge of circuits and symbols.

Enquiry

- What might make a difference to the brightness of the bulb in a circuit? Discuss possible answers. Collect ideas to test practically, e.g. length/thickness/material of wire; number/voltage/size of battery; number/voltage of bulbs.

- Ensure that there is sufficient equipment for the children to work in pairs. They need a variety of wires (different colours, thicknesses, materials), 1.5 V batteries of different sizes, 2.5 and 3.5 V bulbs, and a variety of switches.

- Ask the children to work in pairs and investigate one idea. Help them to formulate their question, e.g. Does the length of the wires affect (make a difference) to the brightness of the bulb? Put their question on a large card on the work surface so they remember it. Predict and test.

- Record results on a table. Discuss how they will reach a decision on what their results show.

- Afterwards, encourage the children to make generalisations using two comparatives about the results of their test, e.g. the longer the wire, the dimmer the bulb; the higher the voltage of the battery, the brighter the bulb. Draw diagrams of their circuits.

Extension Activities

- Remind the children about safety. See these websites: www.rp-l.com/rplkids.htm and www.powerhousekids.com for a safety quiz, information about how electricity is made and games to play.

- Find out the different ways in which electricity is made and how it gets to our houses. A simple and attractive website for methods of production is: http://tiki.oneworld.net/energy/energy.html. Identify nuclear power plants, hydroelectric stations, etc. on a map of the country.

Brighter & dimmer

This is a simple circuit. When the switch is closed the electricity flows in the circuit and bulb lights up. Look at the circuits on the table below. Will the bulb or bulbs light up more brightly than in this circuit, be dimmer or the same brightness? Complete the table below.

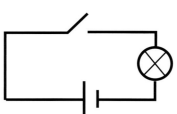

circuit	prediction (brighter dimmer, the same brightness)	reason (hypothesis)	correct (✔) or incorrect (✗)
		because	

NOW!

Make up a circuit of your own. Then ask a friend to predict – will your bulb or bulbs be brighter, dimmer or as bright as the bulb at the top of the page?

Reading and Writing

- Give the children a scenario: There is a problem – the fair is due to open tomorrow and the electric power is not working. Think of five different solutions to the problem, e.g. call in an expert, cancel the opening, delay the opening, buy new equipment, etc. Complete a planning sheet for a story about what happens next (see the display).

- Ask the children to design a character called Robbie Resistance that is operated by electricity. What would they want him to be able to do? Ask them to write a book for younger children entitled *Help! Robbie's lost his power,* or similar, about electricity. Research books for the chosen age group and consider the format (words per page, number and type of pictures, whether words and phrases are repeated, the story itself, the size of the book). Ensure that spellings and grammar are accurate and writing is clear.

- Write about the sound/movements/visual effects in a fairground. Use all the senses to paint a picture in words.

- Find different ways of producing electricity and list the pros and cons of each method. Ask the children to work in pairs – one child selects a method, then tries to persuade their partner it is a good method (whether or not they believe it). Consider the effects of each method on the environment. Use the activity sheet on page 61, which focuses on solar power. Try the website http://tiki.oneworld.net/ for information on alternatives.

- Make a flow chart of one method of producing electricity.

- Write tips for saving electricity in the home or at school.

Speaking and Listening

- Debate how electricity should be produced in the future and the problems with using fossil fuels and the case for and against nuclear power. Research first.

- Make up a play about electricity and safety. Accompany it with electric music. (See page 64 to link with Music.)

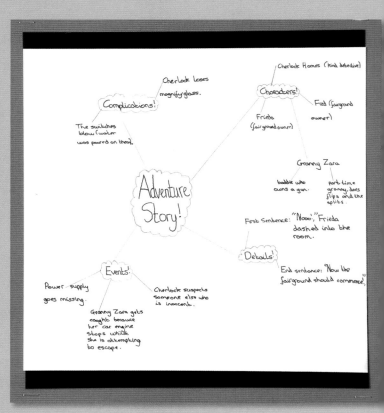

Changing Circuits

Use the power of the Sun!

Solar panels change the energy from the Sun into electricity to heat and light up our houses.

Are they a good idea?

Here is a conversation between a salesman selling solar panels and a builder.

You should put solar panels on your roof. They will provide all the electricity you need for your heating and lighting. Also, they help to protect the environment.

I'm not sure! What about in the winter when there isn't any sunshine? And are they expensive? I don't think we should worry too much about having these panels.

Who do you think is right? If you had a house, how would you like to make its electricity?

NOW!

Find out about solar heating.

Find out about alternative sources of energy.

• Changing Circuits • Belair Curricular-Links Science 6

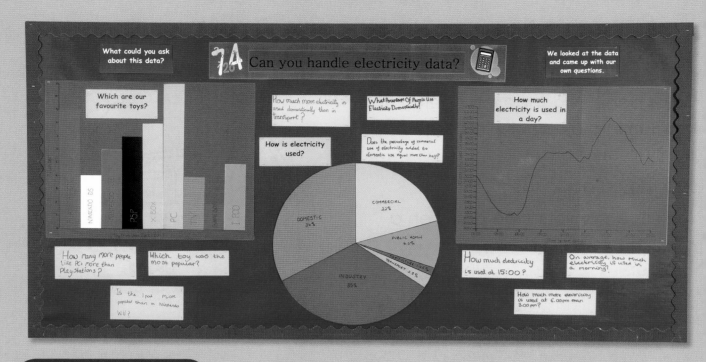

Maths

Handling Data

- Recap previous work on electricity. List different facts about electricity for which we could draw a graph, e.g. Which electrical toys do the children like best? How many electrical toys do they have? What percentage of electricity is produced in different ways? What is the percentage of different users of electricity? How does the consumption of electricity change over a short period of time during a world cup match or televised celebrity wedding, etc?

- In groups, children decide on the type of graph for a given measurement. Discuss when to use a line graph, a pie chart and a bar graph. See the display for examples.

Using and Applying

- List the electrical appliances used in each room of a house or at school. Ask the children to sort these into items that use electricity to produce movement, light, heat and sound. Some devices will produce more than one. Choose a selection and use secondary sources, including the Internet to find out the running costs of each. Which types of appliance use the most electricity? Is a fridge more expensive than an iron? Do bigger items always use more electricity than smaller?

- Encourage the children to evaluate the best deal when buying packs of batteries or other electrical equipment as on the activity sheet on page 63.

- Construct electrical models and use an interface to write simple instructions to control it. Find ways to change the brightness, speed, sequence and loudness of the model.

Understanding Number

- Ask the children to list all the symbols they use in Maths. Exchange with a partner to identify what each one is. Discuss where else in everyday life we see symbols – mathematical or otherwise. (Examples: to give information for safety, advice, rules on the road, etc.)

Does the percentage of commercial use of electricity added to domestic use equal more than half?

How much more electricity is used domestically than in transport?

Changing Circuits

It's a bargain!

Ernie wants to change all his light bulbs at home to energy saving ones.

He needs an amazing 18 bulbs.

He thinks it is a good idea to double this amount so he has spares.

He visits three shops to find the best deal.

SPARKS

Cheapest light bulbs in town!

Packs of 6: £2.40
Packs of 4: £1.80

BRIGHT IDEAS

If you find any cheaper...
...we will refund the difference

**Packs of 12: £5.00
Each: £0.48**

ZIGZAGS

*Don't waste money
Buy from us!*

*Packs of 3: £1.62
Pack of 10: £4.60*

Which shop will give Ernie the best deal?

Remember to think about how many he needs! Use this space to show your working out:

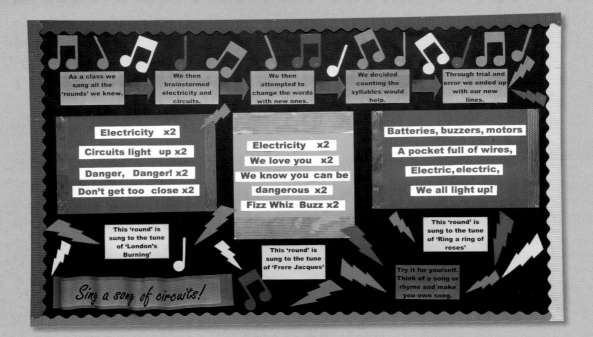

Music

● Make up a song that helps to remember some ideas about electricity as on the display. Here are examples, to the tune of 'London Bridge is falling down':

Electric current flows round and round,
round and round, round and round,
Electric current flows round and round
In a complete circuit.

(about the brightness of a bulb:)
Shorter wires make it brighter,
make it brighter, make it brighter,
Shorter wires make it brighter
So do thick ones.

These could be adapted to cover the speed of a motor, the loudness of a buzzer, etc.

● Think about the uses of electricity and to imagine how it might sound in different appliances and machines. Use instruments to represent ideas. Ask them to try to compose a sequence of sounds to represent, for example, a washing machine cycle (switching on, getting faster, rhythmically tumbling the washing, spinning it and stopping).

Design & Technology

● Design and make fairground rides, vehicles or other machines that are powered by a battery. Use a control box with software to control the models or get the children to devise their own switches to control the movement, such as direction, speed or simple on/off modes. Encourage the children to comment on each other's designs and to suggest ways to improve them.

Art

● Using photos or a trip to a fair, look at the colours, shapes and designs of fairground art on roundabout horses, signs and dodgem cars. Ask the children to design and paint them to fit the shape of a fairground ride.

PSHCE

● List all the devices in their home that use electricity. Ask them to choose one device and write a 'do' and 'don't' list of how to use it safely. Illustrate with examples, such as a parent cutting the cable on the lawnmower or dragging the cleaner by the flex. Be sure children understand safety rules.

● Discuss ways in which we can save electricity and why it is important to do so. Ask the children to devise slogans for the economical, or safe, use of electrical devices, such as: 'Electricity and water don't mix', 'Switch it off', 'Think before you do it', etc. Decide on ways to spread the message, visually or orally. Compare the methods and decide which is the most effective.

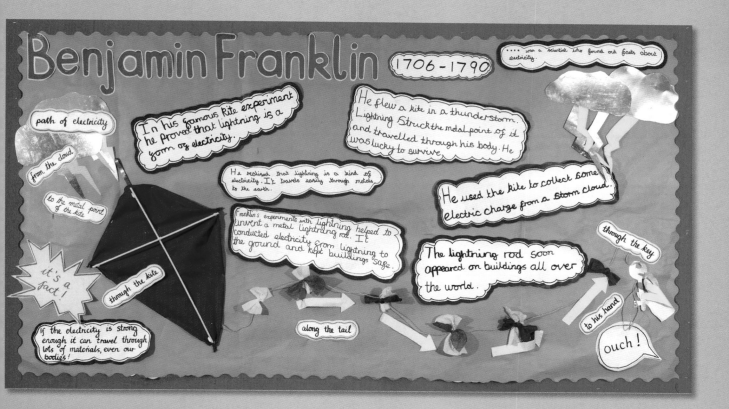

History

- Thomas Edison (1847–1931) is said to have patented 1093 inventions. Find out the meaning of 'patented' and investigate some of his most well-known inventions, including the light bulb. Find out the names of other scientists involved in discovering things to do with electricity.

- Read about Benjamin Franklin (1706–1790) and his experiment with a kite and lightning. Ask, 'Do you think he was lucky to survive?' Present his experiment as on the display above. Use books or the Internet to find out other things about him to add to the display.

- Look at a timeline of inventions in Victorian times and identify those that involved electricity. Ask the children to make up their own electricity timeline from the date of its discovery to the present day.

Geography

- Discuss ways to send a message over a long distance. Ask the children to group them into those that are written, spoken and in code. Which ones are electronic?

- Send and receive email messages to one another. Present six questions, one at a time for a child to send to another and receive the reply. Time how long it takes. Repeat with the children's own questions. Use emails, faxes or other ways to exchange information with a class in another country or region after discussing the information they want and what questions to ask. Discuss which method was the most efficient, and talk about how this would have been done before electricity in use.

PE

- Listen to some electronic music produced by a synthesizer or electric guitar. Encourage the children to move in time to it.

- Choose a variety of different musical genres and ask the children to move in the ways the mood of the music suggests. Encourage them to avoid obvious air-playing guitarist movements and get them to listen and react imaginatively. Make into a repeating sequence in groups.

Changing Circuits

Environmental Enquiry

These grids demonstrate the learning objectives covered in the activities within the theme. The curriculum references indicate the relevant programme of study (PoS) for a subject area unless otherwise stated.

	Learning Objectives	Curriculum References
Science (Page 68)		
Scientific Enquiry (QCA Science Unit 5_6H)	Plan and carry out an investigation into the biodegradability of paper.	Sc1/2a-m
	Discuss issues of caring for the environment and their part in it.	Sc1/1a
	Think creatively about how to solve environmental problems.	Sc1/1a
	Know about 'reduce, reuse and recycle' and its importance.	Sc1/1a
Life Processes and Living Things	Consider the effects of litter on the environment.	Sc2/5a
Materials and their Properties	Recognise and name different materials and their properties.	Sc3/1a
Literacy (Page 70)		
Speaking/Listening and Responding/ Group Discussion and Interaction	Debate how to reduce rubbish.	En1/1a-f;2a-c;3a-e
Understanding and Interpreting Texts	Read about management of different waste materials in own area.	En2/3a-g
Engaging With and Responding to Texts	Use a search engine to find information about litter/materials.	QCA ICT Unit 6D
Creating and Shaping Texts	Write haiku/cinquain/tanka about litter problems.	En3/1a-e;2a-f;12
	Devise a character made of litter.	En3/1a-e;2a-f
	Make a multimedia presentation about litter.	En3/1a-e;2a-f;9b-c; 11;12; QCA ICT Unit 6A
Mathematics (Page 72)		
Using and Applying Mathematics	Interrogate/devise a database about materials.	Ma4/1a;2b; QCA ICT Unit 5B
	Design packaging using as little as possible.	Ma3/1a-h;4/2a-c
Counting and Understanding Number	Understand/calculate percentages.	Ma2/2f
Understanding Shape	Make a recycling Mobius strip.	Ma3/3a-c
Measuring	Measure the weight and volume of waste produced at school/ home and in packaging.	Ma3/1a,b;4a,b
Handling Data	Make and interpret pie charts about the amount of waste produced.	Ma4/2b,c,e,f
	Convert information to bar charts/pie charts.	Ma4/1a;2b; QCA ICT Unit 5B

Environmental Enquiry

Learning Objectives	Curriculum References
Art (Page 74)	
Suggest as many uses as possible for a plastic bottle/paper bag.	PoS 1a-c;2a-c;3a,b;4a,b;5a
PSHCE (Page 74)	
Consider own responsibilities in keeping the environment safe and clean.	PoS 2a,d,h;5a,g,h; QCA Citizenship Unit 02
Discuss and debate reduce, reuse and recycle.	PoS 1;2a-d,f;5a,e
Find out about local issues for waste collection and disposal.	PoS 2a,b
Visit a landfill site.	PoS 1a;2a,b
Suggest how the problems of waste will affect people in the next century.	PoS 4e
Discuss fines for dropping litter.	PoS 2a-d
History (Page 74)	
Use secondary sources to find out about own area at different times in the past.	PoS 4a;5a,c;7; QCA History Unit 18
Describe things that were the same and different at a given time.	PoS 1a,b;2a;4a;5a-c: QCA History Unit 18
Find out what the streets were like when great-grandma was a child.	PoS 1a;2a;3;4a,b;5a-c QCA History Unit 18
Music (Page 74)	
Explore the rhythm of rap songs and make up own.	PoS 4a,b,d;5a,c,e; QCA Music Unit 16
Design & Technology (Page 75)	
Make own rubbish bins for the school.	PoS 1a-d;2a-e;3a-c;4a,b; QCA D & T Unit 6A
Build a moving Litterosaurus from variety of materials.	PoS 1a-d;2a-e;3a-c;4a; QCA D & T Unit 5C
Geography (Page 75)	
Use ICT to write a news report about litter in our environment.	PoS 1c,e;2a,d,f; QCA ICT Unit 4A
Describe a nearby location – its past, present and possible future.	PoS 2g;3a-g;5a,b
Find information about waste disposal.	PoS 1a-c;2g;3a-f;4a,b;5a,b; QCA Geography Unit 16

Environmental Enquiry

Starting Points

- Show the children a message in a glass bottle and in a plastic bottle, washed up on a beach. Discuss why we can still read them. How old could they be? How do we know? What would have happened without a bottle for protection? Would they have lasted on land? Discuss. Introduce the terms, 'biodegradable' and 'non-biodegradable'. Consider other familiar materials and whether they are biodegradable or not (e.g. metals, fabrics, leather, rubber, plastics, wood, paper).

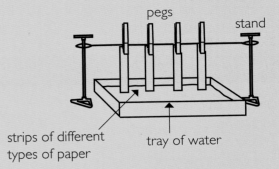

Enquiry

- Ask the children to carry out a fair test to find out how the different papers and the messages are affected by water from the sea, a river or rain.
  - Select at least three different papers use them to set up an experiment, as shown in the diagram. Check that the ends of the paper strips are in the water.
  - Encourage the children to hypothesise by predicting what will happen to each paper strip and why. Decide how and when to record the results. Can the results be put on a graph? Record and compare results with the original prediction.

Extension Activities

- The table below shows the biodegradability of objects made of different materials. Give children the list of materials (use the activity sheet on page 69) and ask them to guess what should go in the second column for each item. Ask them to check their answers using secondary sources. Discuss how the table shows there could be problems in the future. Draw pictures of how the planet may look in 500 years' time if we throw away non-biodegradable materials. Present the children's findings as on the display shown.

Material	How long to decay
Cigarette end	1–12 years
Fruit skin	2 years
Plastic bag	10–20 years
Plastic bottle	will not decay
Glass bottle	will not decay
Leather shoes	30–40 years
Tin can	80–100 years
Plastic-coated milk carton	5 years
Woollen sock	1–5 years

How long will it last?

These are things we throw away.

How long do you think each will last before it rots away?

Predict first. Then use books or the Internet to find out if you are right!

Object	Time it takes to decay	
	Prediction	What I found out
Cigarette end		
Fruit skin		
Plastic bag		
Plastic bottle		
Glass bottle		
Leather shoes		
Tin can		
Plastic-coated milk carton		
Woollen sock		

What advice can you give people about throwing away litter?

Find out which type of litter is the most common.

Find out some interesting facts about the litter we throw away.

Reading and Writing

● Use litter objects and situations as stimuli for the children to write poems with a given form, such as haiku, although it is not essential to keep to the correct number of lines/syllables. Construction and use of language are more important.

– Haiku have 3 lines of 5, 7, 5 syllables, for example:

Plastic bags tossed up Blown in the wind somewhere else Coloured sky rubbish	We're responsible For keeping our country clean Don't drop crisp packets

– Cinquain (below, left) have 5 lines of 2, 4, 6, 8, 2 syllables. Tankas (below, right) have 5 lines of 5, 7, 5, 7, 7 syllables:

Litter Spreads over streets Makes them smelly places Rats foraging for food bringing Disease	If you don't obey and put your rubbish in bins litter police will put a notice round your neck saying 'litter lout was here'

● Devise a litter campaign for a given area. Discuss how to raise people's awareness. Children could devise an interesting character as their logo and a slogan, such as 'Willy wants…' If the area is outside the school, write to the local authorities and bring it to their attention (link with PSHCE).

● Devise a character made of litter and write a story about its work, e.g. how it made a child tidy up their disgustingly untidy bedroom, how it encouraged schoolchildren outside a school not to drop litter. Encourage them to make up a slogan for it. Link with making models in DT.

Speaking and Listening

● Talk about how litter can be reduced. Show a variety of items and ask the children which they consider to be litter (e.g. waste – food, toys, clothes – in the wrong place and caused by humans). Do they consider litter a problem? Hold a group discussion on how to reduce it and then have a feedback session.

● Gather information about materials in the environment and put their findings together as a multimedia presentation. Provide the children with the activity sheet on page 71 which asks them to think about different opinions on the street litter problem, and to present their own ideas.

Let's talk about it!

Look at what the children say about litter in the streets.

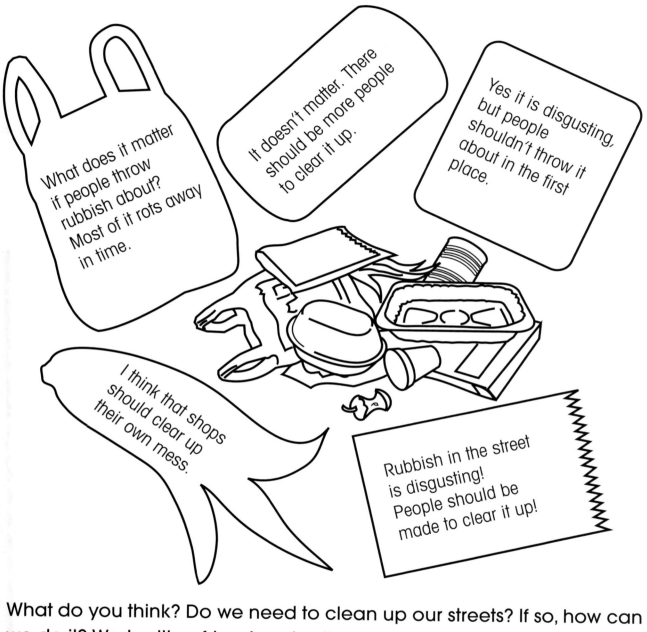

What does it matter if people throw rubbish about? Most of it rots away in time.

It doesn't matter. There should be more people to clear it up.

Yes it is disgusting, but people shouldn't throw it about in the first place.

I think that shops should clear up their own mess.

Rubbish in the street is disgusting! People should be made to clear it up!

What do you think? Do we need to clean up our streets? If so, how can we do it? Work with a friend and write your ideas here.

_____

_____

_____

Choose one idea and prepare a presentation of your argument to your group or the class.

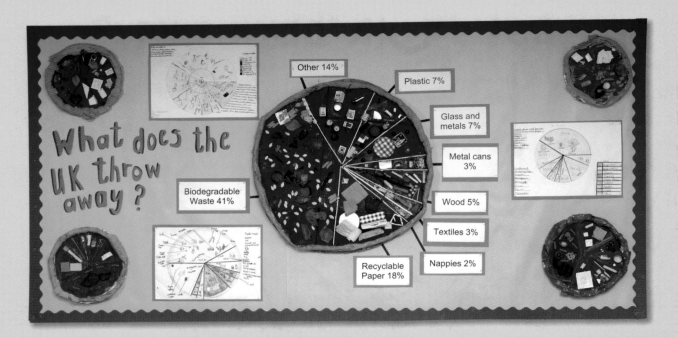

What does the UK throw away?

Other 14%
Plastic 7%
Glass and metals 7%
Metal cans 3%
Wood 5%
Textiles 3%
Nappies 2%
Recyclable Paper 18%
Biodegradable Waste 41%

Maths

Handling Data

- Complete a litter survey. Assign groups to different parts of the school to survey and to record the numbers of waste glass pieces, paper and other materials. After a set period and when sufficient data has been collected, import the data into a spreadsheet program. Use column headings such as date, area, paper, plastic, bottles, glass, etc.

- Draw bar graphs of the results of their litter survey. Get them to exchange and compare information between their groups and interpret their findings. Compare results. Which materials cause the most litter? Discuss solutions.

- Collect information about a range of materials, such as fabrics, metals, plastics. Give the children headings as a focus: how made, uses, biodegradable?, origins (e.g. for metals), other properties. Make up a database. Discuss how to present the information, e.g. use ICT to make leaflets or booklets.

- Bring some things to school, still in their packaging, such as food for lunch, toys and games. Weigh them, then unwrap them and weigh them again. How much of the weight is the packaging? Convert it to a percentage. Ask the children to choose a way to present the information. Discuss whether we always need wrapping or boxes. Ask the children to design a new way to present one of the items but with less packaging. Is it possible? Compare with the original packaging.

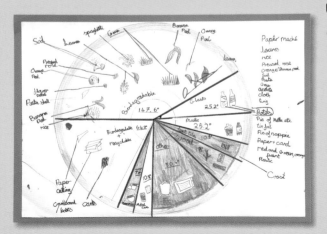

Understanding Number

- Ask the children to find the percentages of litter materials in the school, whole country or region. The recycling activity sheet on page 73 asks the children to convert percentages of a family's litter into graphs and focuses them on how much could be recycled.

- Make up a litter pizza to represent each type of litter as a pie chart for display. Use a PE hoop to represent the pizza, cut out paper to the same size and complete the segments by measuring the correct angles. Stick on the materials before attaching it to the back of the hoop and displaying. Devise questions about the chart.

- Find other examples of pie charts in different contexts. When is a pie chart the most useful way to present information?

What do we throw away?

The Waste family live at 18, Rubbish Tip, Littertown. The town has a terrible reputation for being dirty, with litter everywhere.

The Waste family are trying hard not to be like their neighbours and tidy the town up.

This is the contents of their rubbish bin this week.

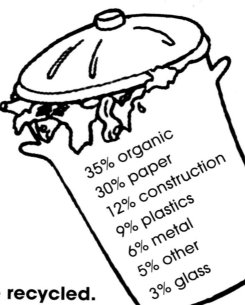

Good for them! They are putting their litter in bins and not on the streets …

Use the percentages in the list to draw a bar graph and a pie chart of the contents of their bin.

But…

35% organic
30% paper
12% construction
9% plastics
6% metal
5% other
3% glass

A lot of the rubbish could be recycled. Find out which items from the bin could be.

Draw another graph to show how much of the rubbish would be left in the bin if they recycled all they could.

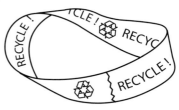

Recycling means that the rubbish goes round and round being made into different things. Her is a simple logo to make to show how materials should be used again and again.

1   Cut out a thin strip of paper. Hold the ends in each hand.

2   Turn one hand over and glue the ends of the paper together.

3   Follow the strip around … and around… and around. This is the recycling message!!

Now make a larger strip and decorate it with an important recycling message.

• Environmental Enquiry • Belair Curricular-Links Science 6

Art

- Collect a range of plastic bottles. Many show what type of plastic they are made of (mainly PET or HDPE, both of which can be recycled). Suggest ways in which plastic bottles can be used (recycled) at home or school, e.g. to make a fish as in the display, a rain gauge, a filter funnel, a container, a pot-pourri holder, a door stop, etc.

- Discuss how a paper bag could be used (e.g. to make puppets, clothes, hats, kites wind socks). Try to invent a new use for a chosen container. It could be extended into a game!

PSHCE

- Screw up waste paper and throw it on the floor. What do children think of this? Where should they put it? Discuss what happens to paper that we throw away.

- Choose places in the town centre to find out where litter collects most – near fast food places/ at bus stops/ outside supermarkets, etc. Suggest why. Ask the police what they do about it locally. How can children help? What other people are involved with clearing litter?

- Visit a landfill site to find out what happens to our rubbish. Discuss the problems in the future.

- **'Littering is a criminal offence. You can be fined up to £2,500, though not jailed. The average fine is around £90, plus court costs.'** This is a statement of law. Discuss whether this is fair or not.

History

- Use secondary sources to find out about own area at different times in the past. It could be about the streets/ town/village/school when (great-)grandma was a child or any time in the past to fit in with other studies. Compare the two times; describe things that we have now that were not present then. What do children think the litter problem was like then compared with now? How have the materials of litter changed between 1950 and now?

Music

- Use a familiar tune, such as *Three blind mice* or other nursery rhyme or familiar song, and ask the children to add their own words about litter.

- Devise a litter rap to advise about reduce, re-use and recycle, and perform to an audience.

Environmental Enquiry

Design & Technology

- Design and make a Litterosaurus out of litter. Find ways to make it move – using levers, cams, etc. Use it to promote discussion and creative writing and speech.

- Make real pizzas from a recipe. Adapt to make different types. Design minimal packaging.

- Recycle old paper into new. Instructions can be found on: www.funsci.com/fun3_en/paper/paper.htm. This website also gives interesting information about the history and production of paper. Try to make different colours by adding food colouring. Decorate with ribbons, buttons, sequins. Change the surface of the paper. How thin can children make their paper? Use recycled paper to make greetings cards or an underwater scene as shown.

- Look at designs of litter bins. What shapes are they? Which shape is the most common? Is there a reason for this? How large is the opening? Design a litter bin. Show its dimensions and a net for making it with instructions. Exchange designs to see if the plan works. Evaluate at end. Design a bag that uses recycled materials. Plan size, materials, type and size of handle. How much will it hold? Test designs to find out how much mass it will hold before breaking. If any are successful designs, they could be produced for sale. Costing of materials and percentage profits could be calculated.

Geography

- Select a local place – a park, part of the school grounds, a path, a pond and put forward proposals on how to look after it. (Link with PSHCE)

- Research newspapers or the Internet to find out about the problems and possible solutions, locally and nationally, of litter and its disposal.

- Discuss the various places to go camping and the difficulties associated with each place. How do campers dispose of litter? Find out the main tourist areas for campers. Is there a problem with litter there? How do the local authorities deal with it? Contact authorities to find out.

- Research the local recycling processes. Evaluate how efficient the recycling process is at school.

- Cut out words and phrases from newspaper magazines and put together to make up a poem about pollution of our world/area. The phrases may not have anything to do with pollution in the magazine but, nevertheless, can be used effectively.

For example – the following are from a single newspaper supplement:

Smaller carbon footprint	**Release the power of Nature**
No compromise	**A city's paradise**
Perfect solution	**New York**
Go greener	**Don't throw it away**
Get fitter	

Revision Games

Dependent and Independent Factors Activity

Children often find it difficult to identify what to change and what to compare or measure when faced with an enquiry question that requires a fair test. They also may have problems formulating a question. The revision game on page 77 can be used to discuss how to formulate enquiry questions and also how to state the factors relevant to a question. Using this type of activity, the children can go on to develop their own questions in different contexts and write a factors activity sheet, like the one on page 77, themselves.

Dependent and Independent Factors Answers from page 77

QUESTION	INDEPENDENT The one thing we change in each fair test	DEPENDENT What we compare/measure in each fair test
1. How does changing the temperature affect how quickly sugar dissolves?	temperature	how quickly sugar dissolves
2. What affects how far a toy car travels from the bottom of a slope?*	not identified	how far car travels
3. Where do we find most snails?	place/habitat	number of snails
4. Does the size of the canopy make a difference to how quickly a parachute falls?	canopy	time taken to fall
5. How long does it take different foods to decay?	types of food	time taken to decay
6. What could make a difference to how well an object floats?	size of bean	time taken to germinate
7. Which length of pipe makes the highest note when I tap it?	length of pipe	pitch of sound
8. Where is the warmest place in the school?	places	temperature
9. What could make a difference to how quickly you run? **	not identified	how quickly you breathe
10. Which of these rocks is the hardest?	types of rock	hardness

* answer could be any of the following: mass/shape/any dimensions of car; surface/number/size of wheels; height/length/angle of slope; roughness/thickness of surface of slope and surface at end of slope
** answer could be length of leg/strength of leg muscles/height/practice, etc.

Vocabulary Revision Game

1. Copy the sheets on pages 78–80 onto thin card and cut out the boxes to make a set of individual cards. Laminate to keep.

2. Mix up the cards and give each child in the class at least one. All should be handed out or the game won't work!

3. Start with any card. The child reads out everything on the card. The child with the answering card reads out what is on their card and so on to the end. It should get back to the starting child. Repeat to see if they can get quicker. Change the cards regularly.

4. To make it easier to start with, each child could write in pencil the answer to their own question on the back of their card to help the game flow.

Dependent and Independent Factors

Fill in each column. Sometimes one of the factors is not mentioned in the question so you need to write this. The first two are done for you. Can you complete the rest?

QUESTION	INDEPENDENT The one thing we change in each fair test	DEPENDENT What we compare/measure in each fair test
1. How does changing the temperature affect how quickly sugar dissolves?	*Temperature*	*How quickly the sugar dissolves*
2. What affects how far a toy car travels from the bottom of a slope?	*Not mentioned – we have to choose one factor to change*	*Distance car travels from bottom of the slope*
3. Where do we find most snails?		
4. Does the size of the canopy make a difference to how quickly a parachute falls?		
5. How long does it take different foods to decay?		
6. What could make a difference to how well an object floats?		
7. Which length of pipe makes the highest note when I tap it?		
8. Where is the warmest place in the school?		
9. What could make a difference to how quickly you run?		
10. Which of these rocks is the hardest?		

Choose one of the factors and make up a question for an enquiry.

Vocabulary Revision Game

I have

EVAPORATION

Who has the name of the process
when a liquid changes to a solid?

I have

FREEZING

Who has the name of the type of change
when a material can change back to
how it was originally?

I have

REVERSIBLE

Who has the name of the process
when water droplets form
on a cold surface?

I have

CONDENSATION

Who has the name of the process when a
solid is heated and changes into a liquid?

I have

MELTING

Who has the name of the process
when sugar mixes with water?

I have

DISSOLVING

Who has the name of the process
to separate rice from flour?

I have

SIEVING

Who has the name of the process to
separate salt solution and sand?

I have

FILTERING

Who has the name of the process
when a liquid is heated and changes
into a gas?

I have

BOILING

Who has the name of a material through
which heat or electricity cannot pass
through easily?

I have

INSULATOR

Who has the name of the property of a
material which does not let light through?

I have **OPAQUE** Who has the name of the type of material which lets heat or electricity pass through easily?	I have **CONDUCTOR** Who has the word, which describes what happens to a material to make sound?
I have **VIBRATE** Who has the word which tells what changes when the length of a vibrating string is shortened?	I have **PITCH** Who has the word which tells what changes when I hit a drum harder?
I have **LOUDNESS** Who has the name of what is formed when light is blocked?	I have **SHADOW** Who has the name of what happens when light bounces off a surface?
I have **REFLECT** Who has the name of the star in our solar system?	I have **SUN** Who has the name of the path of the Earth around the Sun?
I have **ORBIT** Who has the name of the male parts of the flower?	I have **STAMENS** Who has the name of the part of the flower where bees leave pollen?
I have **STIGMA** Who has the name of the process when a seed puts out a root and a shoot?	I have **GERMINATION** Who has the name of the part of the plant that takes in water and nutrients from the soil?

I have

ROOT

Who has the name of the process
by which the plant makes its food?

I have

PHOTOSYNTHESIS

Who has the name of the part
of the plant where most of
photosynthesis usually occurs?

I have

LEAF

Who has the name of the process
in which seeds leave the plant?

I have

SEED DISPERSAL

Who has the name of the part of the
human body which pumps blood?

I have

HEART

Who has the name of the organs
of the human body which
are used for breathing?

I have

LUNGS

Who has the name of teeth
which are used for grinding food?

I have

MOLARS

Who has the name of the teeth
which are used for cutting food?

I have

INCISORS

Who has the name of the teeth
which are used for tearing food?

I have

CANINES

Who has the name of the
types of animals which kill
other animals for food?

I have

PREDATOR

Who has the name of animals
which are hunted by other animals?

I have

PREY

Who has the name which describes
the plants at the beginning of
a food chain?

I have

PRODUCER

Who has the name of the process
when a liquid that is not boiling
changes into a gas?